DISPATCHES FROM THE EDGE

To Dan —
Happy reading
Best wishes

11.1.21

DISPATCHES
FROM THE EDGE

Exploring the limits
of science and the sacred

G. A. TYLER

Boyle
&
Dalton

Paperback ISBN: 978-1-63337-514-7
E-book ISBN: 978-1-63337-515-4
LCCN: 2021910439

Manufactured and printed in the United States of America

For Chris O'Brien
Lux Sono Deo

Contents

We have fallen in the dreams the ever-living
Breathe on the tarnished mirror of the world,
And then smooth out with ivory hands and sigh.

W.B. Yeats

Prologue

I remember a bright fall morning at the Penny Cluse Cafe in Burlington, Vermont. My twenty-two-year-old son Gregory, a piano performance major at the University of Vermont, had just learned that his idea for a senior recital project, a prelude by Russian composer Alexander Scriabin, had been accepted by his faculty advisors. Greg loved the boldness of the piece but hadn't been sure if the music department would accept it as a capstone project for graduation. He'd told me his good news earlier when I stopped by his apartment to drop something off, so a celebration was called for—although we both understood it was really just an excuse for a fancy breakfast.

The restaurant was warm and busy coming in from the October chill. Greg smiled at me as he settled into his seat, his earth-green eyes showing amusement at trading conversation and company for huevos rancheros and coffee. The ease with which his gaze captivated me amid the clanking dishes and bustle froze the moment in time. How could I know him so intimately—since his first moments of life—yet still be filled with wonder in his presence?

We quickly indulged in one of our favorite routines for such occasions: a friendly argument about science, technology, and all things metaphysical, with me playing the role of the boring biologist and Greg channeling his fascination with futuristic techno-physics. The subject was artificial intelligence: is it possible to build a fully conscious robot? If so, Greg asked, how would you know it's a robot? He waved aside my answer when I said I didn't think such a machine could be built, and he asked the question again: "What does it mean when we say something's conscious?"

I said I had no idea what consciousness really was, but rising to the argument, I added the words I knew would egg him on. "Consciousness is a biological force," I said. "And no one has really figured it out yet. You can't design a machine to do something you don't understand. Besides, as far as we know, consciousness requires living cells, neurons. Computer scientists might build a machine that looks and acts human, but appearing to be conscious and actually being conscious are not the same thing."

He smiled. "Okay, that's what I'm saying. How could you tell the difference?"

I remember thinking, *The difference is sitting right across from me—a brilliant young mind captivated by Russian composers,* but sentimental reasoning was outside the bounds of our playful arguments. Besides, I loved that from his perspective as a musician, the idea of grand mathematical algorithms beneath the world's complexity made beautiful, wonderful sense. Anything was possible with the right mix of logic, technology, and imagination. Biology was just nagging details that ultimately are reducible to physics. So why bother? He loved to explain to me how much I didn't know, and I loved to listen.

Breakfast came, and we changed subjects. I asked about a keyboard solo he'd performed on stage with his band at a local club the previous weekend. Was it totally improvised, or had he sketched some of it out beforehand? How did the bass and horns know when to cut in? With great patience he replied, "Dad, it's always improvised. You need to get the feeling of the room." I smiled and didn't tell him how incomprehensible I found it that musicians are able to do what they do. I didn't tell him what a miracle he was to me. For some ridiculous reason there are things fathers can't seem to tell their sons.

Three months after that conversation, Gregory died in his sleep from an obstructed airway caused by complications from strep throat.

In the maelstrom of grief that followed, a dear friend of mine, whose parents had survived German death camps, observed that my wife, surviving son, and I were now facing our own personal Holocaust—an unendurable psychological and spiritual crisis that must somehow be endured. I wasn't sure I could handle it. I didn't know how.

I fell back on my Catholic faith and let it help me absorb all the suffering and terror welling inside me. I didn't expect to find understanding, and I didn't search for meaning. No reasonable parent who's ever lost a child could truly believe that such a painful ordeal fulfills some higher purpose. Being able to silently share my grief was enough. *Enough.* And in the back of the church, as I prayed and sometimes cried, comforted by the ritual of the Mass and responses of the congregation around me, I found hope that I could salvage something of my life for my family's sake.

My sadness and my longing for our beloved son shattered my illusion that the world is a rational, explainable place. I guess I'd always known this, but now I was living it. It staggered me that a person whom I adored and whose physical presence I still felt could simply cease to exist. I was educated as a scientist. I'd long ago lost any illusions that our lives are any more than ephemeral and inexplicable dreams that end in death. But I had always known these things as detached truths, not as conscious day-to-day realities. We're not designed to live that way, but now here it was. "Real" reality was upon me. For the first time the cli-chéd refrain recited in books and movies made sense: The only real thing we can know is loving someone and having them love us back.

I found no great comfort in these revelations. I desperately wished to return to the simpler reality in which my son was still with us and the usual cares of life seemed monumentally import-ant. But that was impossible. I sought insight from the words of poets and writers and turned to anything I could find that offered some small bit of emotional relief. Nothing spoke to my over-whelming feelings of hopelessness and existential despair until someone suggested psychologist Dennis Klass's insightful *The Spiritual Lives of Bereaved Parents*.[1] Reading it helped me realize that I was not alone in my paradoxical sense of feeling alienated from the world but more attuned to what it's actually about. Most bereaved parents experience something similar. Klass suggests par-ents and clinicians consider Buddhism's Noble Truth that all life is suffering, in the sense that life's impermanence inevitably causes suffering. Our natural desire to find happiness and make it last forever is at odds with the way life really is.

This book isn't about Gregory, nor is it about my personal struggle with grief. Even if I wanted to, I don't think I could explain to people who haven't lost a child how his death changed my understanding of the world. But when I returned to work, I realized I couldn't prevent my new sense of reality from affecting my professional life as a science and health writer. The grand scientific orthodoxy I'd embraced as a student had dissipated into the realization that science sees only a narrow bandwidth of what's really out there. I believe most scientists mentally lock this truth away. But the door had now burst wide open for me and I could no more return to that constrained way of thinking than I could banish my despair. But *why?* Why was I comforted by going to church but not by psychological explanations of grief and suffering? Why did the passages in Klass's book about transcendent realities and higher meanings calm my heart and make intuitive sense, but not his clinical explanations of the effects of loss? Why did the ritual of Catholic Mass now resonate with meaning while the "real" world around me seemed shallow and barren? My universe had shifted but I couldn't say how or why. Writers write about things to achieve a higher understanding of the things they write about. I wondered—as a kind of journalistic experiment—if I could write about what theologians call the sense of the numinous, of transcendence and faith, and reconcile it with a scientific perspective. I wondered what the *substance* of such a work should be; then realized I had it right in front of me.

1

Mammalian Weeds or
Homo Religiosus?

What stories do we tell ourselves to explain who we
are? Years ago I worked in a small laboratory on
the research campus of a large pharmaceutical
company in Pennsylvania. Our task was to discover a biochemical pathway for preventing osteoporosis, a disease where bones
become weak from producing too few bone-building cells. We
were particularly interested in proteins that regulate the uptake
and release of calcium in bone and, because the body only produces tiny amounts of these proteins, we had to chemically
synthesize batches of them in the lab to have the quantities we
needed for our experiments.

Because we had the skills and equipment to synthesize cus-
tom-designed protein molecules, we were sometimes asked to
make them for other labs on the campus. That's how I came to
meet Irving Sigal, a brilliant biochemist, a wunderkind, who was
heading the company's AIDS research program. The company,

Merck, Sharpe, and Dohme, had recruited Irving for his ground-breaking work on the molecular biology of cancer-causing onco-genes. When the troubling outbreak of a mysterious immune dis-order morphed into the global AIDS pandemic, Merck went all in to help find a cure and, because viral diseases mimic cancers in the way they hijack our genes, Irving's expertise made him the natural choice to lead the effort.

Our entire lab staff was invited to meet with Irving so he could describe the protein molecules his group wanted us to make. The encounter was staged more like a college class than a corporate conference, with Irving at the front of the room speak-ing as he sketched on a whiteboard the symbolic shorthand of the process by which the human immunodeficiency virus makes proteins after it infects the cells of the immune system.

He could have simply made his request in writing or sent one of his laboratory staff to meet with us. So I believe the pur-pose of this impromptu and much appreciated seminar on the company's AIDS effort was his way of expressing gratitude and scientific solidarity.

The particular details of the meeting have long faded from memory. What's left is my impression of a slender, compact young man with dark hair, an open face, expressive eyes—a soft-spoken and brooding genius, head and shoulders smarter than everyone in the room (and there were some very bright people in the room)—with his voice betraying a hint of impatience over the need to talk down to us while appearing not to do so. Like a second language he could translate in real time the code of nucleotide molecules in the viral RNA into the code of amino acids of the proteins produced by the infected cell. Illuminating what these proteins did, how they transformed the functional biology of the host cell, could point to a possible cure.

This encounter with Irving Sigal was stamped in my memory for two reasons. First, nine months after that meeting he was aboard the plane that was blown up over Lockerbie Scotland by Libyan terrorists. He'd been on his way home from London after delivering a talk to the Royal Biochemical Society. His untimely death was not only a staggering loss for his family and for the research community, but also for the families and loved ones of those whose lives might have been saved had Irving lived.

On a personal and infinitely less important level, meeting Irving that day helped affirm my decision to leave research. I was inspired by the brilliant people all around me, but their brilliance and commitment also compelled me to face the truth, and the truth was that I was good at my job, but not great. I'd never be a wunderkind like Irving, and that was okay. Medical research needs foot soldiers as well as generals and heroes. But as a graduate student I'd felt the first twinges of doubt and guilt that I was taking someone else's place, someone who might also not be a wunderkind like Irving Sigal (few scientists are) but who could make better use of the resources being invested in the work. Medical research is extremely expensive. I'd entered the field from college as a research technician with an idealism that sustained me through many hours in the lab looking though microscopes and mixing chemicals. But at a certain point there was no denying that I liked reading and writing about science much more than the laboratory grunt work. I needed to reconcile idealism with reality. At Merck, I found I liked writing research articles and I particularly liked writing the routine reports required by our corporate overseers, tasks most people dreaded. I liked explaining what we were doing more than actually doing it.

Years later, I'm deeply grateful to have experienced that heady world and for the enduring relationships that grew from it. But even though the chain of editing and writing gigs that became my working life never offered the stability of a research career, I know I made the right choice. And it was in pursuit of an assignment for one of those gigs that the idea for this book first came to me.

Before my son Gregory died, I'd been researching an idea for a freelance project inspired by an assignment I'd taken for a medical software company—an interactive program about depression and antidepressants. As I had brought myself up to speed on leading therapies for depression and mood disorders, I was surprised to read several papers in reputable journals in which the authors speculated that some types of depression might be perfectly natural and not pathological at all.[1] Modern Western culture puts a high premium on personal fulfillment and happiness, but for ancient humans struggling through a subsistence-level existence, fulfillment and happiness were probably rare; vigilance and uncertainty were more the order of the day. A tendency to become depressed under certain conditions might have been coded into the human genome and preserved over time because of the adaptive benefit it provided for our distant human ancestors to help them cope with the harsh conditions of day-to-day prehistoric life. This provocative account of how evolutionary psychology might shed light on a serious medical problem was enough to rekindle my fascination with a subject I'd set aside years ago as an undergraduate student in biology.

I chose biology because I believed then, and still do, that evolution holds the universe's deepest secrets. I suspect that at some point in the hopefully not-too-distant future the scientific establishment will realize that we can learn much more about the nature of reality by studying the story of life on Earth than we can from observing distant galaxies or quantum phenomenon. Astrophysics and quantum mechanics are sexier because they're the unchartered territory at the macro and micro boundaries of physical reality. The problem with "life" from a scientific storytelling perspective is its endless reducibility to intricate cellular processes and molecular cycles. The main story gets lost in the details. Life resonates within us and around us and shapes our existence and so it becomes familiar and mundane.

But the totality of it, the *meaning* of it, remains an exquisite mystery. Creationism and intelligent design are fascinating ideas to ponder as long as we understand there's no scientific evidence to support them so they shouldn't be taught as alternatives to the standard biological version of evolution, which is a complete story unto itself. Creationist arguments tend to be more about sustaining traditional religious beliefs than listening to what the biological story is actually telling us. Even strict materialists who study evolution often admit to an aesthetic sense of creative cosmic genius at work. But it's a hand that works at a metaphysical level beyond belief and beyond biology, that can't be adequately captured by concepts like meaning, purpose, and design—at least not yet.

We've known about evolution for over one hundred and fifty years, and we've been deconstructing its mindboggling, interconnected clockwork—from molecular genetics to oceanic ecosystems—ever since. Yet there's still no universally agreed upon grand vision of what it means, particularly our place in it. We can legitimately see ourselves as the omega of the evolutionary process, as the paleontologist and philosopher Tielhard de Chardin argued; beneficiaries of millions of years of expansion and refinement of animal consciousness; the first species to become aware of its own evolutionary legacy; a tiny pulse of the universe suddenly aware of its own existence. Or we can see human existence as laughably inconsequential—"mammalian weeds"[2] as the great evolutionary biologist Lynn Margulis quipped—lately come and departing soon, choked on our own biological flotsam and self-importance. Both perspectives are equally valid because the subject of the argument transcends our capacity to truly comprehend it.

As a student, the more I learned about evolution the more I became swept up in its metaphysical mystery. The malleability of organic molecules enables copies of the four basic nucleotide units of the genetic code to be assembled into molecular strands millions of units long. The vast number of possible sequences produces a staggering diversity of life forms, from single-cell prokaryotic wonders to multi-cell eukaryotic marvels, all interacting with each other in an incomprehensibly complex and dynamic process begun three and a half billion years ago. This is humanity's *real* legacy, and it baffled me as a college student, as it does now, that more people aren't riveted by it. How can you not want to know how we really got here? What could be more important?

I'd considered pursuing a graduate degree in evolutionary psychology, but at that point it seemed more of a speculative science than a serious research area because, like other psychological sciences, it lacked the tools for connecting brain structure to behavior. Now, as I reacquainted myself with this scientific specialty while researching my project about depression, I saw how refinements in technologies designed for clinical diagnostics and medical research had also provided a new generation of evolutionary psychologists the tools for exploring how the human mind emerged from its primate roots. Computer-enhanced neuroimaging could highlight subtle differences in neurotransmitter-signaling tracts in the central nervous system to show how primitive brain structures had gradually evolved. The availability of rapid, highly accurate DNA sequencing of trace amounts of tissue scraped from fossils could reveal a whole cosmos of information about the biology and ecology of ancient people. Collaboration among specialists in these areas has given rise to "cognitive science," a hybrid specialty that crafts theories about how people think and process information by assimilating findings from anthropology, evolutionary biology, genetics, linguistics, neuroscience, and psychology.

Cognitive science presumes that the genetic code for the neural framework of the modern human mind was set in place over the course of hundreds of thousands of years when our most distant ancestors emerged from other, now extinct, archaic humans. By "neural framework" I mean the intricate, interconnected web of neurons through which trillions of nonstop biochemical interactions give rise to our thoughts, feelings, memories, and perceptions. In fetal development, as neurons proliferate and weave their astonishing web of interconnections, much of what's taking place is directed by a carefully scripted genetic symphony.[3] Part of what those genes are doing is creating the neural templates for the repertoire of intuitive feelings and dispositions required for social interactions. The outlines of our individual personality traits are drawn. The neural structures for reasoning and cognitive information processing are built. The physical complexity of the brain and the inscrutability of the consciousness that emerges from it make it virtually impossible to decipher and trace all these pre-ordained mental tendencies back to their genetic influences. Yet those influences are undeniable.

What cognitive scientists *can* trace are the gradual variations in genes that occurred during the evolutionary transition from ancient archaic humans and other primates to modern humans. By matching these variations with information anthropologists have unearthed about the behaviors of those distant beings, cognitive scientists can learn how changes in the genetic code might have shaped the modern human mind. One of their most ambitious and controversial efforts seeks to answer a question that anthropologists and behaviorists have been asking for decades: Why are human beings also inherently *religious* beings?

People have been creating and practicing religions for tens of thousands of years. It's such a prevalent and enduring feature of the human race that some anthropologists have wryly suggested that our species name should be changed from *Homo sapiens* to *Homo religiosus* to highlight our uniqueness as evolution's first and only religious life form. Theorists hypothesize that the pervasiveness of religious behaviors in ancient and modern humans alike means that religion must have provided an important social benefit in an era when the human mind was still being shaped by the necessities of subsistence and adaptation. They've also observed that certain religious ideas become widespread and get passed along and modified by language and culture because they seem to engage innate mental operations in emotionally powerful ways.

The importance of this relationship between cognitive tendency and social benefit is demonstrated by the persistent willingness of humans to expend vital resources and creative energies to actualize their beliefs, from the earliest cave paintings and bone sculptures to Stonehenge, the great pyramids, and the magnificent cathedrals of Europe.

The idea of studying religion through a cognitive science-evolutionary lens fascinated me, but it also struck me as a teleological sleight of hand—defining something not on the basis of what it is but by what it does. "Religion exists because it serves a purpose" or "religion exists because of the way the human mind works" might sound innocuous enough, but there's a powerful undercurrent of scientific overreach: Science can now explain all you need to know about religion and, therefore, the science vs. religion debate is officially over. Now it's just a matter of filling in the neurocognitive blanks. This seemed a little too slick.

I once attended a lecture by an evolutionary psychologist who explained why people like some paintings more than others. Certain combinations of colors appeal to us because they reflect patterns found in nature, he explained. Good paintings align with our innate sense of balance and proportion. Representations of people and nature must match our intuitive expectations. We especially like landscapes with greenspace, open vistas, and a lake or stream because our distant archaic ancestors felt safe in such environments. I remembered thinking, this might make sense for landscape paintings and portraits, but what about Picasso's fractured black and white pastiche of war and suffering? What about van Gogh's serene French village beneath a swirling, malevolent cosmos? What about da Vinci's portrait of a young Italian woman gazing back at us from her distant world? What can evolutionary psychology tell us about all that?

Judging from the vast literature on the subject, evolutionary psychologists would have lots to say about the cognitive processing involved in producing and experiencing works of art like *Guernica*, *Starry Night*, and *Mona Lisa*.[4] And they could certainly explain how those cognitive systems evolved for more mundane adaptive purposes. But the creative spark that drove Picasso, van Gogh, and da Vinci to explore transcendent themes eludes rational analysis. The neuropsychology of the creative process remains enigmatic. Brain scan studies of people considered to be creative geniuses suggest that the creative process involves many areas of the brain, and not a particular brain structure or locus. Great creativity seems to arise from making associations and connections that aren't readily apparent to others. We can't explain the inner workings of creativity. It's not a rational process. But we accept its legitimacy, as expressed through works of art, literature, and music, to inspire us or reveal self-evident truths about the world or the human condition.

We should afford the same tolerance to the imaginative creativity of religious belief argues Tina Beattie, a professor of Catholic studies and prolific writer on religious ideas. Creativity is a more fundamental human attribute than rationality, she says. The transcendent urge that fuels creative expression was first kindled into being by the awakening of early humans' religious imagination as demonstrated by prehistoric paintings in the caverns of Lascaux and Altamira. Here, says Beattie, we see the emergence not only of *Homo religiosus* but of *Homo creativus*, the first and only being who tries to capture its dreams of material horizons beyond its own existence.[5] Science seeks to privilege rationality as humanity's greatest intellectual endowment, but our creativity is the most "primal" expression of who we really are. If we believe great works of art and music can communicate meaning and truth that elude rational analysis, Beattie asks, then why not see them as legitimate ways to speak about transcendence and God?[6] Religious *and* scientific authorities get it backwards when they minimize the role of creativity and imagination in religious experience, as they too often do, argues Beattie, and ascribe more importance to the internal rationality of doctrine and dogma.

I agree. Our fascination for creativity and wonder energizes our religious experiences. Remove the imaginative dimension and what remains is a shell of exotic claims that can be rationally examined and, therefore, explained away. And that's precisely what cognitive theorists were doing in the papers and books I was reading such as Pascal Boyer's *Religion Explained* and Richard Dawkins's *Outgrowing God*. In these and similar works the authors sought to explain religion in terms of social benefits, cognitive tendencies, and rational self-deception. In their minds, the outlines of what religion "is" were now firmly in place, and it was just a matter of backing up their theories with more data. It also struck me that these authors didn't or wouldn't acknowledge how their steadfast atheism influenced how they approached their work: if they were religious practitioners themselves—if they believed in God or the possibility of God—they'd intuitively understand why other people believe in God and would appreciate that there's a valid subjective dimension to religious belief that can't be reached by objective scientific study. Evolutionary biologist Stephen J. Gould made a point of exploring how his Jewish-yet-non-religious upbringing influenced his worldview, in Rock of Ages, his exposition on "science and religion in the fulness of life." Gould affirmed his non-belief but insisted on approaching religious faith with open-minded skepticism because, as he put it, truly and rationally one can never know.[7] But no such self-effacing grace or acknowledgment of covert prejudice was forthcoming in the works of the foremost cognitive theorists I was reading. I felt intellectually stifled by all this. But I also recognized that these were bright people from prestigious institutions making bold claims about something fundamental to human existence.

And so I needed to understand more. I needed to study their studies and deconstruct their reasoning. I needed to understand why their claims had triggered a storm of pro and con books and journal articles from other scientists and scholars. I didn't know where I was going with this self-enlightenment project. Besides satisfying my own curiosity I sensed there'd be a good story for a popular science article or blog. But I also knew that it would be a challenging story to write. I'd need to educate myself to the point where I felt comfortable guiding readers along a safe path through this scientific labyrinth without getting lost. At this point I'd already read neuroscientist Andrew Newberg's *Why God Won't Go Away*, his amazing overview of the interface of neuroscience and religion, and science philosopher J. Wentzel van Huyssteen's *Alone in the World*, his powerful, scientifically astute argument for the uniqueness of the human mind as a natural phenomenon. Both those authors asked the same question that the cognitive scientists of religion were asking—Why are human beings also religious beings?—but came to radically different conclusions. So, why were these cognitive theorists and writers so determined to legitimize a new, science-based atheism? Was that the pulse of the story?

And it was at this point, with lofty thoughts of articles and interviews and big ideas soaring through my mind, that Gregory's death shifted the world beneath me and I dropped into darkness.

Philosopher Ludwig Wittgenstein said, "We are asleep. Our life is a dream. But we wake up sometimes, just enough to know that we are dreaming." How true. My grief over my son's death had awoken me to "real" reality, away from the thoughts and cares that routinely occupy our lives. We use our imaginations to plan our futures because in imaginary worlds life follows a predictable arc. But in this new reality I saw that logic and reason are woefully inadequate tools for understanding who we really are and what's really going on. In real reality you need to learn to use a different part of your brain.

Psychologists believe traumatic stress and prolonged grief can cause emotional detachment from reality. They argue that this detachment is a defense mechanism and an ingrained self-preservation strategy to dissociate from reality when reality becomes too painful to bear. This makes sense as long as we accept that we all share a standard version of reality from which we can become detached.

But an alternative view is that some life events can awaken us to a version of reality that's more authentic, even though it's profoundly more difficult to bear. Rather than being detached, we're awakened. We see the importance of trying to achieve, more than anything else, a certain grace in our lives. I often feel like I left my old self behind when I found Greg on that cold, terrible morning. Both he and I departed from our previous world. A different person now stumbles along the trajectory of my former life, heartbroken, grief-stricken, but more fully human. I've met other grieving parents who, like me, now have a different perception of time because the past acquires heightened importance and the future, we now see, is pure illusion. I often like to imagine that I'm a time traveler and can circle back to a moment when Greg and I were having lunch somewhere and arguing about something important. I know those moments of connection between us were real and live forever in reality. A beautiful folk song by the British composer Sandy Denny, "Who Knows Where the Time Goes," speaks to the elusiveness of time in the face of enduring love. As the world endlessly transforms itself, the object of love may be lost, but the love endures and grows stronger.

The thought I'm trying to express is that sometimes we experience occasions of great insight in which we see the world with renewed eyes and unbiased clarity, and awaken to something that I think we all intuitively know: There's meaning in the world that can't be grasped with reductive reasoning. The more tightly we try to bind it with words the more elusive it becomes.

It was with those eyes that I began to reread the materials I'd collected about the cognitive science of religion. After a while, I realized that the pulse of the story wasn't the pros and cons of a new scientific theory that can explain religion. The pulse of the story was a question: Can science infuse our religious beliefs with deeper meaning? We are *Homo religiosus* because we're biologically driven to understand why we're here. It's the highest, most defining thing we do. Science can help us find our way by explaining what religion is *not* and by unmasking the cognitive biases and self-deceptions that lead to dead ends.

But how does one write a science-referenced narrative about something that ultimately isn't about science? I had no idea. The science writer's prime directive is to make things as simple as possible but not simpler, as Einstein supposedly said. You must write what you know, and I knew very little about the theological "magisterium," to borrow evolutionary biologist Stephen J. Gould's gorgeous word.[8] And so I started reading theology and talking to theologians. One thing led to another. I had a wonderful conversation with Rabbi David Novak, a professor of Jewish Theology at the University of Toronto, about his essay on the sanctity of human life and his idea that morality without metaphysical belief is ultimately groundless. Based on this conversation I was inspired to read Novak's address[9] to *Die Weisse Rose Stiftung* (The White Rose Society), a German-American foundation dedicated to commemorating the White Rose Group, a coterie of student activists at the University of Munich in the 1940s who protested the Nazis' persecution of Jews and other minorities. One of their leaders, Sophie Scholl, a national hero in modern Germany, was captured and interrogated by the Gestapo, and, on the basis of her Christian beliefs, chose to be executed rather than recant her denouncement of the fascist government. She was twenty-two when she died—the same age as Greg. Her story inspired me and gave me the idea of infusing my own story with some cultural and political relevance rather than sticking with the detached, academic tone that I'd been wrestling with. To me, her actions showed that abstract belief is anemic and only comes to life through words and deeds. Her metaphysical belief and her physical courage formed a holistic unity. We can only understand belief in its real-world context.

I learned that there's a dynamic, intellectually rich global community of religious philosophers very much in tune with modern religious practice and modern scientific insights, and with lots to say about both. The fact that this surprised me revealed some of my own bias that religious and theological thinking were stale and self-absorbed. I saw how clueless and unenlightened many scientists who study religion were about the nature of religious belief. I learned, for example, that most contemporary theologians hold that proof of God's existence has nothing to do with searching the cosmos or quibbling about scientific theories. The important theological debates of our time (and I'm simplifying) start with the premise that God's existence is a felt presence within our conscious minds, not a reasoned belief we acquire through religious indoctrination. Religion helps cultivate our native awareness of this transcendent presence. But without this nucleus of inner awareness, religious doctrines and practices alone are meaningless. Belief in God means recognizing this presence within you. It's not about an unseen external force that runs the universe and manipulates human events. There are, and always have been, progressive movements in each of the monotheistic traditions that claim true connection with God requires purging one's mind of superstition, anthropomorphism, and idolatry.[10] Cognitive scientists and evolutionary psychologists who focus on religion don't seem to know this. It surprised me how many serious scientists who study religious behavior cling to the culturally popular idea that grand scientific discoveries in astronomy and evolution have irreparably cracked the foundations of established religion. Some scientists are genuinely baffled that religion still endures despite these factual setbacks, as if religion were some kind of theory resting on

22

evidence. The undistilled message of contemporary theology is that God is associated with the very nature of our being; God is not an objective fact adrift in the physical universe. To atheists who derisively say that scientists have searched from subatomic particles to galaxies and found no trace of God, contemporary theologians would answer: "You didn't look in the right place."

I also realized that the traditional "science versus religion" debate is outdated. The important debate of our time is how should religion and science redefine themselves in the postmodern era. Religious extremism and terrorism have accelerated the decline in faith in traditional religious institutions. The horrifying abuses to which scientific knowledge was applied in the last century have fractured the long-held Enlightenment belief in the inevitable scientific progress of human civilization. Science doesn't automatically bestow its practitioners with morality and wisdom. Scientists are no longer the unquestionable arbiters of intellectual truth, passing unbiased judgment on the fitness of philosophical and theological ideas. As someone who fell in love with science at a young age and made a living at science-related endeavors most of my life, I've found these things difficult to accept. But I've gradually come around to agreeing, like it or not, that scientists can't detach their personal beliefs and biases from their understanding of the world, even at the highest levels of theoretical thinking. Just because you've disciplined yourself to be objective doesn't mean there's such a thing as perfect objectivity. This might be possible for Buddhists attempting a state of meditative mindfulness, but not for scientists contemplating natural phenomenon.

I've also come to realize that science will never produce the all-encompassing narrative of the universe it once promised.

Instead, science has revealed a bewildering house of mirrors, with infinite multiverses and unfathomable black holes reflecting alternative and unknowable versions of reality. The late Stephen Hawking's Grand Design Theory, which claimed, among other things, that God wasn't necessary to explain the origins of the universe, is receding into the archives of fanciful cosmic musings dating back to the ancient Greeks that say more about the historic era that produced them than the actual state of intergalactic affairs. Some of his most devoted followers say Hawking should have left God out of it.[11] Science should have nothing to say about God's existence.

I've had these realizations along with millions of other scientifically trained and scientifically inclined people around the world, and I believe many of us now see that science can't provide the metanarrative of existence that might have once attracted us to it. But it *can* help us write our own metanarratives. The difference is subtle but important. It's fine to be an atheist or nihilist, but don't blame science. Science can *inform* your atheism or nihilism, but it can't be the source. Scientific reason rests on infinite reduction, one thing reducible to its underlying processes, trailing off into mathematical unprovabilities. It reveals relationships among phenomenon that can be expressed symbolically. Science is a way of seeing the universe, a tool. But it's a deconstruction tool, not a meaning-making tool. It can't provide us with meaning because it wasn't designed to do so. When we gaze through the scientific lens for meaning "out there" in the universe, we're looking in the wrong place. What many contemporary theologians are saying is that we should be looking within ourselves with full appreciation for who we really are. Our vision shouldn't be clouded by the universe's vast eternity and our own ethereal brevity. Humanity is as much a part of the universe as black holes and galaxies and, as many would argue, it's we who give the universe meaning. Within us the universe becomes aware of its existence; when we ascribe meaning to our existence we're ascribing meaning to the universe.

Cognitive science and evolutionary psychology illuminate brilliant pathways for helping us learn "who we really are." But influential writers in these fields turn off the path when they blur the lines between the statistical observations they've made and the personal, anti-religious biases they've brought to their work. They have a right to express their views as long as readers and students of their work fully appreciate what's being left out and what's *not* being talked about. Providing this missing perspective was an impetus for this book.

I believe one of the most important things they're not talking about is the relative scale of biological complexity. For example, infectious disease experts can provide reasonably comprehensive explanations for why some vaccines work and others don't. There's much more to learn about the cellular and molecular biology of the immune response, but we have a pretty good grasp of what we know and, most important, what we don't know. The same relative degree of certainty applies to many other realms of scientific study. But when cognitive scientists and psychologists make claims about the human mind, they're talking about a biological dimension that's orders of magnitude more complex than the immune system and other biological systems. How much they *don't* know is profound. Cognitive scientists and psychologists understand this and take it for granted, but many people who read their work don't. This is why I've introduced a bit of the background biology of cognitive science into the conversation.

I know I can't transcend my own narrative framework as someone educated in the biological sciences, and so the audience I had in mind for this book are those with science backgrounds who, like me, enjoy reading about philosophy, spirituality, and theology but often find that contemporary writers in those fields have a somewhat naïve understanding of the scientific view on controversial subjects like evolution and neuroscience. If you don't have a science background, I hope this book gives a taste of how scientists tend to look at things. I'm not claiming to represent the scientific community's views. It would be a ridiculous claim to make because there never has been and never will be such a thing as a single, coherent scientific "view." But we do tend to look at things differently. Nor am I promoting a grand scheme of metaphysical or religious belief. I wouldn't know where to begin. What I've tried to do is describe a few of the essential debates at the confluence of evolution, faith, and psychology through the words of some of the most brilliant contemporary minds engaged in those debates. I hope that in some small way this will help inform your own narrative of meaning.

2

"Am I therefore become your enemy, because I tell you the truth?"

On December 16, 2015, Wheaton College in Illinois, a Christian evangelical school, suspended political science professor Larycia Hawkins for posting an image of herself on her Facebook page wearing a hijab and proclaiming that American Christians should "stand in solidarity" with American Muslims to protest bigotry and persecution of religious minorities.[1] Hawkins was responding to Republican presidential candidate Donald Trump's calls for closing mosques in the United States, rejecting refugees from Islamic countries, and requiring American Muslims to be registered on a special government watch list.[2]

Hawkins planned to wear the hijab through the Christmas Advent season. As she explained on her Facebook page: "I stand in human solidarity with my Muslim neighbor because we are formed of the same primordial clay, descendants of the same cradle of humankind . . . I stand in religious solidarity with Muslims

27

because they, like me, a Christian, are people of the book. . . But as I tell my students, theoretical solidarity is not solidarity at all. Thus, beginning tonight, my solidarity has become embodied solidarity."[3]

The school claimed Hawkins hadn't "faithfully represent(ed) the College's evangelical Statement of Faith."[4] Islam and Christianity share common biblical roots, the school's communication office explained, but "we believe there are fundamental differences between the two faiths, including what they teach about God's revelation to humanity, the nature of God, the path to salvation, and the life of prayer."

The Bible *appears* to be open to interpretation, the college was saying, but only the Christian evangelical understanding of the Bible and the doctrine derived from it provide access to God, personal salvation, and redemption. A professor at a progressive Christian evangelical college like Wheaton should encourage students to explore other interpretations and appreciate the theological richness of our ancient Christian roots. But "religious solidarity" with Islam was taking it too far. Hawkins's social media post seemed to imply that Wheaton was comfortable having its faculty teach religious relativity over specificity; the college was most definitely *not* comfortable with this. Hawkins felt her actions embodied her beliefs; the college administration felt that firing Hawkins embodied *their* beliefs.

Hawkins's firing sparked campus protests (although some praised the school's actions) and triggered an eruption of mainstream media editorials and social media rants about the nature of God and the universality of religious worship. For a brief but remarkable moment the national news cycle took a theological turn and gamely explored some of monotheism's most ancient disputes: Was Jesus an earthly embodiment of God or a divinely inspired prophet? Can people who don't accept the word of the Gospels and salvation through Jesus still experience divine truth? What does Islam teach? Is there only one path to God? Didn't Christ command his followers to love all people, even those outside the faith?

In truth, Hawkins wasn't arguing for moral or spiritual equivalency between the two religions. She was really saying that people of all faiths must stand together in the face of persecution of any religious minority. It was the religious equivalent of Benjamin Franklin's "We must all hang together or most assuredly we shall all hang separately."

Her actions spoke to my heart because of all the regressive things Trump was promising to do if elected, stigmatizing America's Muslims—"othering" them through official government policy—was particularly appalling. By denying the diversity and humanity of Muslims and signaling his willingness to consign them all to a homogenous subclass of suspicious others, Trump was demonstrating his showman's grasp of the power of fear and paranoia. It was a willful display of bigotry unseen in modern national politics. Its tragic effectiveness was demonstrated by the wave of counter protests it triggered on campuses across the country.

In another time and political era Hawkins's actions would have been a perfectly reasonable thing for a professor at a theological college to do. Academic idealists must be willing to avow their beliefs beyond safe academic walls. They should be willing to put their reputations and, in Hawkins's case, their careers on the line (although many shy away). She sought to remind us that the shared God of Christian, Islamic, and Jewish monotheism demands believers show mercy and compassion for all humans. It's not enough to only give lip service to such beliefs; we must be ready to rise up against intolerance when we see it happening around us.

During a less politically fraught time, Wheaton College might have reprimanded her but not fired her. But these aren't ordinary times. The intolerance expressed by candidate Trump, which inspired Hawkins's protest, reflected America's lingering anxiety about the threat of Islamist terrorism and how best to respond to it. Despite all the misery and violence that's been inflicted on Muslims in the Middle East since the 9/11 terrorist attacks, there's still great mistrust and mixed sympathy in the west for people of *that* religion. Many of those who praised the college's firing of Hawkins did so not out of agreement with its stance on evangelical purity but in support of a presidential candidate who was openly vowing to trample the human and legal rights of Muslim Americans. Hawkins probably wouldn't have caused the same stir had she simply stated her position in a newspaper op-ed or academic journal. But she understood the power of the image, and the image of a black female professor at an evangelical college wearing a hijab on Facebook was bound to grab national headlines.

But in many ways, this highly charged clash of religion and politics also "embodied" a fascinating but highly esoteric debate taking place outside of popular culture among scholars and scientific specialists, which, simply stated, asked the same question some media pundits who covered the Hawkins story were asking: Is the human mind designed to imagine God or to perceive a God who exists?

Investigating the Numinous

Evolution remains an unsettled and unsettling subject in the public realm, but in the academic world, particularly in the behavioral and biological sciences, the truth of evolution has been established beyond all doubt. There are still many unsolved questions within evolution's theoretical framework, just as there are lingering questions within the frameworks of quantum theory, relativity theory, or atomic theory. Not surprisingly, one of evolution's biggest mysteries is how early human history shaped the modern human mind.

Larycia Hawkins's wonderful, metaphorical "primordial clay" stands for the Biblical mystery of human creation. The image is of God reaching into the vibrant mud of the new Earth and pulling forth the progenitors of the human race, of whom each descendent would be made in God's image and, down through the ages, harbor intuitive knowledge of God's presence and a capacity for right and wrong. If we transcribe the metaphor in evolutionary terms, we might envision the million-year history of human evolution as the primordial stew that gave rise to modern humans. But what about humanity's intuitive knowledge of God? There's a scientific narrative for that too.

The first psychologists to study religion used theologian Rudolf Otto's Latin term "numinous" to describe the quality of the conscious state in which people feel a sense of transcendence or connection to a non-physical presence that's at once within oneself and beyond oneself; a sense of the divine, the holy. Numinous feelings didn't directly translate to belief in God, but for religious practitioners they seemed to be the driving pulse of their belief. The role numinous consciousness played in each person's psychic life was influenced by their intellects, personality traits, and unique cultural environment. For some it might become the focal point of devout worship; others might learn to suppress and marginalize it within their waking thoughts.

When scientists acquired the technical means to go beyond speculation and observe how religious experiences affect the physiology of the brain, they saw similarities in the brain scan patterns of devout followers of different faiths. The volunteers who participated in these studies all tended to report feelings of transcendence, timelessness, spacelessness, connection to something beyond themselves, and oneness with humanity and love of others. Because these subjective feelings appeared linked to reproducible patterns of neurobiological events, some psychologists suggested that the human brain seemed hardwired to believe in God. Variations in these neural signals among individuals seem to have less to do with their particular faith or denomination and more to do with the depth of their belief and their life commitment to religious practice.

These imaging studies weren't intended to say anything about the legitimacy of religious belief. As one neuroscientist quipped, a brain scan of a person eating apple pie doesn't prove the pie actually exists. But they did show that the neuropsychology of religious experience could be studied in a serious way. Standards could be established; observations could be shared; theories could be formulated. More important, these early findings demonstrated that religion was *something* but not *anything*. Atheists often popularize their non-belief with cynical claims that any loosely connected set of superstitious nonsense can qualify as a religion because if people are just making it all up then religion can be whatever they want it to be. But here was evidence that religion, like language, appears to be associated with a distinctive neuropsychological signature with preferential activation of certain brain areas over others. Religion is "something" because it's associated with a unique state of mind. If we all evolved with the same neurological equipment from the same primordial clay, then this unique neurological ability must have evolved along with us.

New Interest in Ancient Faiths

It's tempting to think that these kinds of neurophysiological studies, popularized in books like Andrew Newberg and Eugene d'Aquili's *The Mystical Mind* and *Why God Won't Go Away* might, on their own, present opportunities for the kind of interfaith dialogue Larycia Hawkins was alluding to in her protest. For example, how could someone claim their intolerance and acts of violence are rooted in their faith if it can be shown that "real" religious faith flows from feelings of oneness and connection to others? But neuroimaging technology is a limited tool. Only in science fiction and the popular imagination can it explain human behavior. Observing the movement of blood and electrons in the brain provides an intriguing biological signature of what religious experience looks like, but not much more. It may tell us that religion is "something," but it also says there's no difference between religious faiths. Is that an acceptable idea? And why did this capacity evolve in humans? What adaptive purpose does it serve? Other *kinds* of studies were needed to fill in the gaps.

Coincidentally, just at this moment of rising scientific curiosity, the Al-Qaeda attacks of 9/11 triggered a global demand for psychological profiles of religiously inspired extremism, corresponding to (and partially funded by) the Bush administration's War on Terror.[5] As one psychologist of religion recalled, before 9/11, he and his fellow researchers comprised a small, insular community who largely kept to themselves. After 9/11, the international mainstream of psychological research turned its full gaze to religion, with particular interest in anti-social, extremist, and terrorist behavior. Published scientific studies relating to religious belief increased by as much as four- to six-fold annually.[6] From my review I would characterize much of this as agenda-driven research focused on supporting and testing prevailing ideas.

Some investigators and scholars in this post-9/11 wave seemed to view Islam as a kind of psychological gateway drug inevitably leading to addictive, mindless fanaticism—as if the terrorist's homicidal state of mind was somehow qualitatively different than that of a Christian or secular mass shooter. Many approached their work with similar views about Christian evangelism and fundamentalism. The thinking seemed to be that deconstructing the common psychodynamics of religious faith might help authorities identify individuals who've been "radicalized." New academic journals emerged to give researchers platforms for sharing ideas about the underlying psychology of religious belief and its social and cultural effects. It wouldn't be correct to characterize all of this activity as a direct response to Islamist extremism. But the unexpected resurgence of religious conflict in the age of digital enlightenment roused the global scientific community to the fact that religion, to paraphrase poet Dylan Thomas, was not going to "go gentle into that good night." The unspoken but prevailing scientific wisdom prior to 9/11 held that science had long ago refuted all the world's ancient creation myths and claims of invisible spirits running the universe. We were living in a post-Christian era and we thought the rest of the world was moving with us from religion's dark shadows into the light of liberal atheism. Now, suddenly, we woke to the realization that billions of people, many of them well educated and scientifically sophisticated and living among us, still clung to their beliefs. Religion continued to be a potent influence in culture and politics. There was growing realization that religion is a deeply imbedded psychological and social phenomenon worthy of serious study.

Can Cognitive Science "Explain" Religion?

Much of the information that emerged as a result of this surge of scientific interest stuck to describing the neural and psychological processes associated with religious behavior and, as with earlier neurophysiological studies, made no judgements about the authenticity of religious claims. They sought to understand *how* and *why* people perceive God; not *if* the God who's being perceived actually exists. But cultural fervor over the danger of politicized religious beliefs set the stage for an aggressive new scientific atheism which sought to demolish the traditional boundaries between science and religion. The gloves came off. These new atheists argued that all religious belief is a kind of emotional disorder which can be attributed to cognitive and psychological miscues. Religiosity, they declared, is "caused" by an overly charged, evolutionarily honed tendency to see meaning and purpose in events that, logically, have no real meaning or purpose. By explaining why we're naturally prone to making such mental mistakes, cognitive science can help end our childish enchantment with God and other superstitions.

Cognitive anthropologist Pascal Boyer's *Religion Explained* was one of the pivotal works along these lines.[7] His impressive attempt to explain away God by explaining the evolutionary psychology of religious belief provoked a fury of counterclaims from fellow scientists and theologians. Many questioned Boyer's interpretations of his findings. Others said his portrayal of religious belief was one-dimensional and tended to conflate cultural tropes and superstitions with serious philosophical concepts. Yet, his insights about the adaptive advantages of agency detection—perceiving the presence of an intelligent agent, regardless if one actually exists—and how we use it to build narratives to cope with the unknown raised important questions about the nature of religious belief versus superstition. At what point does human free will take over from an inherited behavioral tendency? His careful explanation of how evolution shaped the mind to process information in ways that predispose us to religious behaviors challenges religious practitioners to question how they can know authentic spiritual truths from cultural influences. We don't need to embrace his atheistic conclusions to recognize the value of his arguments.

A Natural Body and a Spiritual Body

These cognitive theories of religious belief seek to burst the bubble of practitioners who logically accept evolution as factual truth while believing that something magical happened in the course of human evolution—a biological Deus ex machina. God either directly intervened at some point or set the process in motion in a way that bestowed us with souls and free wills and spiritual insight. Somehow, through God's hand, intelligent apes became spiritual beings. This makes the material version of biological evolution a kind of backstory we can all comfortably live with. After all, didn't the Apostle Paul tell the people of Corinth "There is a natural body and there is a spiritual body" (1Cor. 15:44 KJV). Most of the world's denominations have adopted some variation of this "accept it but keep it at arm's length" approach.

But cognitive scientists like Boyer are saying God didn't intervene because "God" is a figment of a mental process that gets some things right and lots of things wrong. Because we have language and culture, we codify these useful cognitive figments and pass them along. But we must now see, say the theorists, that these cognitive mechanisms that arouse suspicion and infer agency are survival mechanisms that arose in the mammalian brain long before we arrived on the scene. It's time for us to see ourselves as we really are.

Most practicing Catholics, Jews, and Protestants accept the general outlines of biological evolution without worrying too much about reconciling human uniqueness with the material evidence that the only thing separating us from lesser animals is a few lines of genetic code. Despite all the factual correctness of evolution, we can trust our belief in God as authentic because we know what's in our hearts and mind. But cognitive scientists are saying they too know what's in our hearts and minds. They can reach into our heads and show us why our deepest beliefs and spiritual insights are deceptive and not authentic. Scanning the brains of religious practitioners only tracks the outer, neurobiological signs associated with their thoughts. Neuroscientists rely on the people being scanned to report what they're thinking about. But cognitive theorists are inserting themselves into the internal mental space of religious believers. Moreover, they're saying the believers themselves are engaging in self-deception so their verbal accounts of their thoughts can be misleading.

At first this cognitive critique of religious belief sounds intellectually intimidating, but it has some serious gaps of its own, which I'll describe later. For now, let's take a broader look at the evolutionary narrative on which it bases its theories.

We now irrefutably know that our distant-but-anatomically-similar ancestors existed side by side with other species or subspecies of archaic humans who looked very much like us and had many, and in some cases most, of our behavioral and mental characteristics. They were "humans" but they weren't "us." They possessed varying amounts of intelligence, imagination, and self-awareness, but not to the extent and proportion of modern humans. They probably loved their children and may have gazed at the stars in wonder. Some exhibited traces of moral behavior and buried their dead equipped for an afterlife. But they didn't practice religion as we would know it. They didn't and couldn't produce a Bible or Koran. They didn't possess our intellectual acuity. They didn't appear to have symbolic reasoning and other higher cognitive processes associated with religious awareness. They may or may not have had spiritual lives. So, were those distant related cousins *Imago Dei*, made in God's image? Did they have souls? Or did their slight differences of anatomy and intellect disqualify them from God's grace? I'm aware of no religious doctrine that's come to terms with these questions.

Moreover, anthropologists will probably never be able to say exactly when, where, and how anatomically modern humans first emerged as a distinct group during their evolution in northwest Africa. But anthropologists *do* know that it happened gradually, not suddenly and miraculously. Speciation doesn't happen magically. New species of animals with new physical and behavioral traits don't suddenly appear, and this most certainly didn't happen with humans. God extracted us from the primordial clay not all at once but slowly, over hundreds of thousands of years from a host of other Homo relatives. Biology is flux and process. Diversification into species and subspecies occurs gradually over many generations and cycles of reproduction. Given the wealth of data that scientists have accumulated about early human history, there's less and less room for a narrative that envisions a sudden direct intervention by God. The idea that fully modern humans with souls and spiritual minds spontaneously emerged from nature can no longer evade the factual truth. If religious faithful insist that scientific atheists must account for the free will and intuition of human consciousness, then cognitive scientists of religion have a right to insist that religious believers come to terms with the factual truth of human evolution and how it challenges the idea that we appeared on the earth as a discreet and intentional act of God. But rather than accept these two incompatible narratives as they are, let's consider how some scientists and scholars have reframed these contradictory claims in ways that open possibilities for reconciliation and deeper insight. The first step is for religious practitioners to move beyond the idea that their faith prevents them from acknowledging the facts of material evolution.

Evolutionary biologist (and practicing Christian) Joan Roughgarden makes the excellent point that much of the essence of Jesus's teachings was about grasping the ethical principle behind a parable or rule and not about strict adherence to a code of behavior or insistence upon an inviolable set of facts. Eating with unwashed hands doesn't defile us, nor does the food we put into our mouths. What defiles us are the hateful words that come out of our mouths. Much of Jesus's dialogue with his followers was about personal enlightenment, seeing beyond one's prejudices, seeking the truth. Jesus would be aghast, says Roughgarden, if he saw people denying a factual truth such as evolution, in his name.[8]

It's a bit presumptuous to say how Jesus would react to anything, but I agree with Roughgarden's sentiment. One doesn't come away from the Gospels with a sense that Christ desired his followers to be close-minded, dogmatic, and incurious. If evolution attempts to describe the sublime process by which God brings life to the world, and if its study has been honestly and truthfully pursued, which it has, then it makes no sense to deny it on religious grounds. As Paul asked the Galatians: "Am I therefore become your enemy, because I tell you the truth?" (Gal. 4:16 KJV)

"Am I therefore become your enemy, because I tell you the truth?"

Limits of the Scientific Narrative

So how can the facts of evolution with all they imply about the shaping of the cognitive human mind be reconciled with religion, which by necessity insists that there's something truly unique about us—that we are *Imago Dei*, made in God's image?

Time won't change the fundamental principles of evolution as first observed by Darwin, but the overarching narrative will undoubtably change with regard to the emergence of animal consciousness as a non-material driving force within the evolutionary process. As we'll see, the factual story of evolution is still so incomplete that we don't even know how much of the story is missing. But the immediate problem with the evolutionary narrative—and I say this as one who deeply respects scientific rationality—is that the scientific lens with which we decode material reality, is a *perceptual* lens. It perceives things a certain way. It's a gem, but it's not the perfect diamond we imagine it to be. The scientific version of evolution will always come with its own self-limited narrative.

It's first necessary to remember that science—a way of seeing and describing the world—unintentionally but invariably produces narratives of how the world works. As philosopher Mary Midgley wrote, the story of evolution can never be an inert piece of theoretical science because scientists themselves, along with everyone else, inevitably attach meaning and significance to things. We think symbolically, so we can't avoid symbolism. The evolutionary narrative gives us a certain world-picture. There's nothing particularly wrong with this, said Midgely, as long as scientists recognize these tendencies in themselves and how they influence their theories.[10] Midgley also made the excellent point that nature is vast;

what scientists choose to investigate, they choose for their own reasons, informed by their own ideas and perspectives.[11] When I read the books and studies of cognitive theorists of religion, I understood that they were investigating these phenomenon precisely because they knew this was a controversial and culturally fraught subject. They didn't just stumble upon it. They certainly didn't commence their work expecting to uncover unexplainable supernatural mysteries; they commenced their work expecting to fill in the blanks of their own broader, vaguer narratives of human evolution. I believe the results they've reported are accurate and their interpretations are reasonable within the framework of their methods. But we can't avoid questioning how their expectations influenced what they looked at and what they chose to ignore.

Many writers believe it's not the facts of science, but the unintended narratives science brings with it that put it in conflict with western religious beliefs. Science deconstructs the world in ways that are communicable and, therefore, reproducible. That's its true power. But this also means that scientific ideas are conditioned by the thought processes of scientists, even down to the level of individual nuances of grammar, vocabulary, and syntax—the kinds of things, according to cognitive scientists, that vary from one person to another and influence how we understand the world.

Science has long stood on the proposition that its practitioners can learn to suppress their own subjective biases and approach their work with machine logic detachment. Grammar, vocabulary, and syntax can be harnessed to a different yoke. The peer review system provides intellectual guardrails to keep the reasoning pure. Other endeavors might be vulnerable to cultural influences and self-deception. Not science. Science is righteous. Correct?

"Am I therefore become your enemy, because I tell you the truth?"

Enlightenment's End

No one denies the efficacy with which scientific knowledge can be used to manipulate physical reality. Scientific reasoning permeates civilization at all levels, and the technology it produces drives the global economy. Its righteousness as a force of material wealth is justified. But its efficacy with deciphering living systems, particularly human behavior, is still a work in progress. Despite a century of prodigious research, the complexity of the human mind remains the black hole of behavioral and social theory; the unfathomable singularity at the center of the show. Science has given us the tools to make our lives safer and more materially comfortable, but not to help us know right from wrong and who we really are. Science can tell us how to build a global communications network and tame pandemics that would have wiped out earlier civilizations; but it can't tell us how to control our darkest political urges.

More surprising than our overconfidence in science for deciphering the mind (no one really thought it would be easy) has been our serious miscalculation of the complexity of evolution and inheritance on the molecular biological level. Contrary to mid-twentieth century dogma, we now know that "epigenetic" (i.e. nongenetic) processes play a major role in development and inheritance and, therefore, evolution. But we've barely begun to explore the vast number of different epigenetic systems out there and how they interact. Directly related to this has been our catastrophic mistake of underestimating the complexity and interconnectedness of ecological systems. As sociologist Raymond Murphy wrote in Rationality and Nature, twentieth century futurists and social prophets believed our scientific knowledge was nearly complete.[12] The limitless technologies it provided would allow us to socially reconstruct nature; seize control of its gradual, mindless evolution and bend it to our needs. No longer would humans succumb to famines and plagues. The massive population growth this spurred could be serviced and provided for with new technologies that transformed natural resources into endless amounts of energy and other consumables. But we hadn't anticipated the impossibility of bringing decimated ecosystems with million-year pedigrees back to life. In our enthusiasm to expel nature from the dynamic of human history we ignored that most basic of biological principles: all living systems produce waste. Capitalizing our production and consumption was easy; capitalizing our waste management—not so much.

Our faith in the inevitable moral progress of human civilization, born of the Enlightenment but with modern science leading the way, was also shaken by a century of global wars and genocidal horrors perpetrated by secular, "post-Christian" regimes seeking to impose ends-justify-the-means ideologies on vulnerable populations.[13] As Timothy Snyder, historian of the Holocaust observed, those regimes conflated science with politics to create total ideologies that sanctioned mass murder as justified by the forces of history.[14] German fascists believed their actions expressed evolutionary "survival of the fittest" logic; Russian and Chinese Marxists understood their genocides as necessary embodiments of irrefutable natural principles that guided human history. Scientific discovery drove an apocalyptic-themed Cold War pitting capitalist and Soviet philosophical systems against each other, which both sides waged with moral certitude. Contemporary critics of religion have successfully disseminated the bogus idea that religion has been a chief cause of war and human suffering down through the ages. In truth, while religious disputes most certainly helped spark wars and brutality in the distant past (although there were usually political, racial, and economic factors as well), taking religion out of the equation has made things much, much worse. Moreover, religious minorities have often been the chief victims of post-religious regimes in their pursuit of enlightened social transformation.

In our own time, "science" has alerted us to the grave danger posed by environmental degradation and climate change, but we forget that it was the technical application of scientific knowledge that produced the toxic chemicals and released the carbon dioxide. Science gave us knowledge of material reality we weren't politically smart enough to handle.

Scientific knowledge alone is innocuous. But within the collective western consciousness we've witnessed the ease with which scientific information and theories can be misappropriated and misused. We've discovered what we should have known all along: Science is reflective and unpredictable.[15] It carries along with it no inherent morality. It might provide a beacon of enlightenment to lead us from the muck of human history, but it might also provide a means and excuse to inflict suffering on unprecedented scales. The irony (and danger) of expecting psychological and social sciences to rescue us from Islamist terror at the start of the twenty first century shouldn't be lost on us. And if the emerging new cognitive theory of religious belief—really just an updated version of Marx's "opiate of the masses"—infiltrates the academic establishment, how might it filter its way out to twenty first century political and social policies? As Tina Beattie speculates in *The New Atheists*, as we become more secularized, will we also become more stridently atheist? And if the perceived threat of religious extremism within our political landscape grows and traditional religious belief is viewed more as a social liability than a source of tolerance, will we see the willful elimination not just of those beliefs, but of the people who hold them?[16]

I don't share Beattie's concern that new cognitive theories and new atheism pose an existential threat to traditional religious establishments. The intellectual richness of Christianity, Islam, and Judaism have helped them weather harsher storms. But as historians of religion like Karen Armstrong have argued, these great world religions have survived and thrived by facing the philosophical challenges that buffet them, not by wrapping themselves in the brittle and ultimately vulnerable armor of extremism and fundamentalism. The existential challenge they face is how to maintain their transhistorical dignities—not cheapening and relativizing their message—while offering spiritual triage for a culturally fractured, suspicious, and cynical world.

The Postmodern Disruption

With my quick sketch of recent history, I've tried to encapsulate the arguments of contemporary writers who say the social catastrophes of the twentieth century contributed to the loss of confidence in traditional sources of scientific, political, and religious authority and transformed us from a modern to a "postmodern" society.

Postmodernism isn't an ideology as much as it's a reflective and summarizing philosophy. But its relevance to the traditional "science versus religion" debate can't be overstated. Postmodernists argue that the twentieth century's master narratives of history, religion, and science only served to sustain economic and political power structures, which ultimately proved disastrous. Moreover, the "truth" those narratives offered was self-serving and could never actually be true because, in truth, there was no "truth"—just hegemonic, high-minded, subjective interpretations of a world we can never really know. Postmodernists say all such narratives exploit our natural tendency to believe there's an objective world outside ourselves—one that exists apart from us and in complete indifference to us—that can be known and understood in common terms. But, in fact, each of us can only ever know our own self-serving version of the world.

It's easy to understand why most scientists dismiss postmodernism as academic liberal bluster. Besides being tangibly confirmable and provable, the objective blueprint of the material world science has created over the last century—even if it's still very incomplete—has brought unprecedent levels of health, wealth, and security. From a rationalist perspective postmodernism is elusive and fickle. I loved reading the sixteen excellent but densely reasoned essays in *The Cambridge Companion to Postmodern Theology*, which examined the interface of postmodern uncertainty and Christian doctrine.[17] Yet I came away with no sense of coherence and structure. Other postmodernist tracts left the same impression. I'm sure the authors would explain that their emphasis on individuality and context was exactly the point. Their goal isn't to build yet another rationalist philosophical system but to

help us understand the intellectual moment we live in and to lib-
erate us from destructive and oppressive ways of thinking. I'm
not sure they've succeeded on either count, but they have reasonable things to say about the prejudicial and oppressive uses of
high-minded systems of knowledge. Their critiques spoke to the
transformation of traditional religion, but their anti-rationalist
message implicates the scientific community as well.

Scientists can't dismiss the currents of aloofness and elitism
in scientific communities or deny that scientists often equate their
highly specialized knowledge with a position of intellectual privilege and judgment. Scientists allude to the truth-seeking purity
and stringency of their methods; the peer-reviewed certainty of
their insights. Yet scientific paradigms—like all other knowledge systems—eventually decline and change. Scientific careers
get staked to theories that are later proven wrong. And scientists
can't deny the ingrained tendency to side with liberal and progressive political causes, which is fine, but it has allowed conser-
vative and authoritarian political leaders to blur the lines between
legitimate scientific concern and liberal political activism. If scientists wonder why their warnings about looming environmental
catastrophes and global pandemics aren't taken more seriously,
they shouldn't so readily dismiss postmodernists' insights about
what happens to the "truth" when virtually all information can be
commodified and personalized.

Postmodernism is relevant to the grand debate of religion
and science because it claims both sides have built solemn tem-
ples from baseless fabric. The truth systems of science and religion
exist mainly in our heads. All we perceive comes to us as bits of
information through our imperfect senses to be processed by our

imperfect minds. Religion's grand cathedrals and science's grand theories are, ultimately, social constructions meticulously crafted and adjusted over time to privilege one way of seeing the world over others.

Some writers point to the metaphysical mystery of quantum physics, on the microscopic level, as proof that the scientific version of physical reality is a shapeshifting illusion.[18] Since physicists first came upon quantum phenomenon in the 1920s, they have wrestled with the disturbing revelation that subatomic particles seem to possess a range of different properties and occupy various states of organization until they're measured. The act of observing and measuring them "collapses" them into specific positions with definite properties. This implies that physical reality has no definite structure until we observe it. If we accept this as true, then we must also accept there's no disembodied unified reality beyond our senses.[19] If we reject it as an anomaly of how we see things, then we must live with the idea that there are theoretical limits to what we can know about the world.[20]

Physicists don't dispute quantum metaphysical weirdness. But they say postmodernists misunderstand quantum theory and overlook its mathematical complexity. We may never solve quantum mysteries but that doesn't mean all scientific knowledge rests on an illusion or that physical reality is no more than a social construction. They say quantum irregularities are too puny to trouble the physical laws that most of science deals with.

I agree. At best, quantum uncertainty provides an analogy for how specialized ways of seeing the world might shape our perceptions. Science—and religion—seek to fix certain worldviews and collapse them in our minds as correct and true to the exclusion of all other worldviews. While postmodernists might not get all their science right, their overarching critiques of science can't be totally dismissed. Scientific paradigms shift the same way that religious beliefs change. It's very possible that twenty first century research will fracture sacred, twentieth century scientific dreams of a unified theory of everything—from quantum mechanics to multiverses. If the non-science, anti-religion philosophers of postmodernism are correct, and neither religious revelation nor scientific investigation can ever provide us with something that is absolutely and universally "true," how do we form a meaningful picture of our existence?

Francisca Cho, professor of Buddhist studies at Georgetown University, says the problem is not with how we construct world-pictures, but with our western expectations of what our world-pictures are supposed to do. Buddhists understand that we exist in a realm of fluctuating phenomenon, says Cho. Postmodernist rejection of all knowledge systems is dangerous and nihilistic—how can we live in such a meaningless world? [21] Disciplined knowledge systems of science and religion can guide us and help us create positive, socially constructive ways of living in our world of fluctuating phenomenon and coping with its uncertainty and built-in suffering, she says. The question isn't about the existence of a disembodied reality outside ourselves, says Cho. The question is how we use language to help us visualize and understand that phenomenal reality. Western science long ago became "obsessed" with the idea that language could be stripped of all its subjective biases and creative uses and be deployed in ways that strictly describe an objective, non-human world, she says. [22] Today, given the highly contextualized uses of language among scientific specialties, we should know better. Yet this misguided idea still troubles our dialogues and disrupts our perceptions. Buddhism places no such expectations on language and emphasizes, instead, the skillful and beneficial use of language in different contexts.[23]

Buddhist wisdom judges the value of a world narrative "on its own terms" and not whether it supports or contradicts other world narratives, says Cho. We don't need to embrace all of Buddhism's beliefs and traditions to make use of this intellectual tool.[24] We don't need to accept or refute whether reality exists apart from us. It's more important that we awaken to the limitations of language to answer our questions and fully capture that reality (if it exists) and, perhaps, become more accepting of the idea that it might be better captured by "narrative pluralism."[25] Within the boundaries of this pluralism lie opportunities for new and meaningful reconciliations between western religion and western science.

A Pluralist Reconciliation?

How could pluralism help us reconcile a materialist version of human evolution with a religious view that humans are distinctly made in God's image? The scientific facts of evolution don't support creationism or intelligent design, but accepting the factual truth of evolution doesn't mean it can't be contextualized or visualized in non-scientific ways. Cho says our puzzling, western belief that science can reveal the "truth" to the exclusion of all other ways of knowing the world prevents this from happening and has fueled a kind of "evangelical fervor" among scientific purists who insist on a strictly atheistic interpretation of evolution.[26]

I agree. Their fervor isn't justified. It's correct that modern humans adapted their way into existence from their proto-human ancestors over thousands of years. But that truth doesn't entitle scientists to claim that the evolution story alone can explain things that are far beyond its capacity to explain. We're decades and perhaps centuries from fully understanding evolution on all its biological levels. The story is far from complete and shouldn't be hijacked to promote cultural agendas.

Francisca Cho argues that science inevitably succumbs to the temptation of framing its grand ideas as narratives.[27] I think she's overstating things a bit. I'm not sure there's a coherent narrative of organic chemistry, for example. But she's correct in saying, like philosopher Mary Midgley, that the facts of evolution unavoidably imply a narrative that encompasses our existence. And, right now, with our very incomplete picture of evolution, the essence of the narrative is that human existence is biologically unremarkable. I agree with many writers who not only see this as a destructive narrative, but who believe its weaknesses jump off the page. No other animal has possessed our degree of self-awareness, intelligence, and symbolizing skills. How this came about—the transformation from pre-modern to modern human—remains a mystery. When did it happen and how? We can set aside creationist ideas of divine intervention and other extra-biological events. But as a science writer trying to summarize the literature on the subject, I'm convinced we'll never pinpoint a distinct transformative moment when Homo sapiens became Homo sapiens *sapiens*, Homo *creativus*, and Homo *religiosus*. Our evolutionary story is an incomplete story of becoming that's still very much in progress. More biological information won't reveal a magical moment when non-humans became humans, but as our knowledge of evolution matures, we could see the kind of revision in comprehension that occurred when Einstein took us from a mechanical universe to a relative universe. We might come to see human evolution as an epochal and singular event, with the same metaphysical significance as the initial emergence of life from the primordial clay. For now, if the material narrative says our existence has no great significance within the framework of biological evolution, yet we intuitively sense there's something wrong—and potentially self-destructive—with this conclusion, then we've begun to see the limitations of the material narrative, and why religious narratives told in different ways in different frames of context and reference are necessary. We cling to a dangerous illusion when we cling to our belief that there can be a unified master narrative of science that makes all other narratives unnecessary, says Cho.[28]

From her perspective as a Catholic writer, Tina Beattie says the postmodernist claim that economic and political ambitions have influenced the western science paradigm is true, but this doesn't delegitimize science to the extent that postmodernists allege. Science is obviously much more than a socially constructed way of relating to the material world, she says.[29] It has transformed our understanding of nature, and we in the western world live longer, healthier, more comfortable lives from the technology it has provided.[30] But in the process of this intellectual transformation many scientists have sought to assume the cultural role that religious leaders once held as custodians of the one and only truth, says Beattie. This is bound to be a cultural and philosophical dead end because the scientific way of knowing the world doesn't encompass all the ways that human consciousness can know the world. Science is a means to an end, but it shouldn't be the end in itself, says Beattie.[31] It can inform our world picture, but we mustn't let it provide our only world picture. The postmodern critique is correct in its charge that science doesn't exist apart from cultural influences, and that the practical applications of scientific knowledge can be exclusionary and prejudicial, says Beattie. Our great task is to broaden its context so that it helps us achieve our dreams rather than serving the interests of a narrow hierarchy and thereby becoming the master of our dreams.[32]

In the postmodern era of cynicism and context, science and religion face the same challenge of proving they can put us in touch with an objective reality outside our own heads, says Beattie.[33] I believe this is an excellent observation with real world implications. As the 2020 Covid pandemic spread across the country we saw wide resistance to pleas from public health officials to wear masks and practice social distancing to help slow the spread. Political leaders, including the president, challenged the universal truthfulness of the science, often coming up with their own pseudo-scientific claims or peculiar interpretations of the data. Many people on the political left reacted to this by proclaiming that we must all "believe in science" but I think they missed the point. The anti-maskers weren't rejecting "science." They were rejecting a particular version of science they didn't like. This revealed the dark side of postmodernism: When there's no ultimate truth and no ultimate truthmaking authority, we're each free to pick and choose the "science" that supports our personal beliefs. There was no shared idea that a consensus of scientific authority might be the best bet when faced with an environmental or public health threat, and no shared understanding of our biological vulnerability.

I believe traditional religions face a similar problem that science faces, which Beattie has described in The New Atheists. By exposing hierarchies of social bias, postmodernity has done more for gender, racial, and religious equality than the rationalist Enlightenment. But what happens when all authority and knowledge systems are suspect? If we believe everything is conditioned by context and individuality, and the only truth is that there is no truth, how does the socially progressive west come to terms with marginalized people whose religious truth, for them, isn't relative and conditional, but inviolable and sacred? At what point does the postmodern reverence for difference and customized identity hollow out everyone's values and rob everything of meaning?[34]

Beattie questions the prospects of the postmodernist trend towards a new spirituality informed by science but dismissive of traditional religion. Focusing on the flaws and scandals of contemporary religious institutions obscures the fact that these ancient traditions of faith represent "millennia of wisdom and reflection on the human condition." Spirituality and mysticism without religious concepts to organize and communicate their ideas "are not necessarily avenues to peace," she warns.[35] How will Christians of the post-modern era transform the diverse voices of marginalized people into new visions of Christianity? How will they accommodate conservatives and fundamentalists who don't share their view that religious beliefs are contextual and relative? Postmodernism "flourishes" in the shadows of a nihilism it denies, says Beattie. Walking the line between tolerant inclusivity and reactionary conservatism means embracing the positive aspects of secularism while keeping its nihilistic message at bay.[36] It won't be easy.

I believe Larycia Hawkins' protest illustrates Beattie's point. By appearing in a Hijab and elevating Muslims to the same spiritual status as Christians, Hawkins challenged all our prevailing culture tropes. Evangelical Christians interpreted her message as promoting religious relativity, and her protest flew in the face of right-wing political designs to marginalize and "otherize" Muslims. But she also offended the sensibilities of many feminists and progressives who see the hijab as a symbol of male oppression and who struggle to understand how a woman might willingly choose to veil her features as an expression of religious faith. Liberal ideology celebrates multiculturalism as long as none of the cultures being celebrated bear the stamp of traditional religious belief. As Tina Beattie argues, the postmodernist version of tolerance struggles to accept genuine and meaningful difference.[37]

What are those meaningful differences? How can we know what's true and meaningful when we're made to doubt all our traditional narratives of religion and science? The scientific story of human evolution is incomplete but perhaps exploring it in more detail can help us discern between those things in traditional religious narratives that are self-deception and those things, as Francisca Cho says, that can help us create positive and constructive ways of living in this astonishing world.

3

Exocentricity

E arly in her career as a primatologist, Jane Goodall drew criticism from other scientists for her practice of naming rather than numbering the chimpanzees she was observing in the wild. She was anthropomorphizing her experimental subjects, said her critics—characterizing their behaviors in human terms. Not keeping a proper scientific distance.[1]

Nonsense, said Goodall. When chimps were obviously being affectionate, jealous, or spiteful, why not say so? Why not use our own primate minds to recognize the actions and motives of other primates?[2]

When she observed a group of chimpanzees erupt in a display of what appeared to be feelings of awe and delight as they came upon a majestic waterfall in the Kakombe Valley in Tanzania, she characterized their movements as a kind of dancing and speculated that this might be a display of proto-religious behavior. She wondered if they too were responding to yearnings over nature's wonder that inspired the first religious behaviors of early humans.[3]

As an animal rights activist she was particularly concerned about the fate of chimpanzees used in medical research. In her autobiography she recalled an encounter with a young male chimpanzee, JoJo, isolated in a cage in a basement lab at New York University. Other chimps were nearby, but JoJo couldn't touch them, groom them, tussle with them. His entire world had only ever been clanging steel doors, screaming chimps in other cages, artificial light. Goodall recounts that tears welled in her eyes as she leaned forward to greet him. Gazing back at her, JoJo extended his fingers through the bars and touched her cheek where the tears ran into the laboratory mask she was wearing. She recalled imagining that St. Francis was looking down upon them and he too was crying.[4]

Goodall's heartrending words reveal not only her compassion for the young chimp's obvious emotional suffering but her sense that something was profoundly wrong—spiritually profane—about exploiting an innocent, intelligent, self-aware being this way.

Her groundbreaking insights that chimps exhibited human-like personalities and behaviors to a much greater degree than previously believed rocked the scientific establishment. Chimps may lack our structured, symbolic language, so they can't communicate their motives to us. But Goodall intuitively grasped the presence of conscious awareness and cognitive processes very similar to our own.

Distant Cousins?

Goodall's specialty, primatology, provides valuable insights about human evolutionary history because chimps, humans, and a handful of other primate species emerged from the same pre-primate ancestors about five million years ago (chimp and human DNA are 99 percent the same)[5]—a blink of an eye in evolutionary time. Around that time the human limb of the great ape tree, the *Hominina*, began to separate from other primates and branch into at least ten but perhaps twelve or more different species of Homo—highly intelligent, self-aware, tool-using, bipedal, and intensely social human-like beings. One line of those beings gradually transformed into us, anatomically modern humans, somewhere around two hundred thousand years ago. The biological story of our emergence from this "archaic human" host is muddled not from lack of information but, paradoxically, from too much scientific proficiency, which keeps clouding the picture with new physical evidence and genetic details. For example, several of these species interbred, most notably Neanderthals and modern humans. Mating between separate species usually doesn't produce viable offspring, but mating between some archaic human types clearly did produce viable offspring, so it's not clear if they should all be labeled as separate species or subspecies within a species.

These biological details may be sorted out eventually, but what's clear now is that all archaic human species evolved in Africa, and at least two of them, Denisovans and Neanderthals, migrated into the Middle East and then on to Asia and Europe hundreds of thousands of years before our own ancient ancestors made the same journey somewhere around sixty to a hundred thousand years ago.[6]

These scientific findings seem to undermine religious claims that human existence was somehow intentional. If just a few minor tweaks to the Homo genome separate us from lesser beings with no souls and no mental ability for religious belief, and those tweaks happened randomly, how can any religious doctrine claim that a divine being intended our existence? Creationists argue that modern humans were the inevitable product of the evolutionary process set in motion by God. When anatomically modern humans finally emerged, they were infused with souls and the mental capacity for spiritual faith. But as Jane Goodall's observation of the chimps in the Kakombe Valley suggests (as do many other behavioral and anthropological findings) other primates, and particularly those of the *Hominina* branch (our branch), seemed to possess some traits and behaviors we would classify as "proto-religious," to borrow Goodall's terms. This suggests our modern human religiosity is just a finely tuned version of a mental trait that was already present in our distant ancestors. In fact, current anthropological theory suggests that this is exactly what happened. The underlying tendency of religious behavior was cultivated and enriched by the gradual development of symbolic reasoning and language in early Homo sapiens. In other words, modern human religiosity occurred as part of a heterogeneous process, not as the intentional act of a supreme being and, therefore, all versions of traditional creation myths are wrong, no matter how metaphorically we interpret them. But this is a false dichotomy between intended creation and genetic haphazardness. And it glosses over the question of human uniqueness—are we just a highly successful version of Homo, nothing more? Or is there something different about us?

It's impossible to scientifically prove that human religious behavior was either an entirely random event or an inevitable product of primate evolution. Genetic studies of living populations clearly show trends in evolutionary direction. Genetic analysis of distant and mostly extinct species is extremely difficult, but it's reasonable to suggest that once the Homo genome was established millions of years ago, there was very likely a trend towards greater cognitive capacity that inevitably led to us. But biologists can correctly claim that had environmental circumstances been slightly different at any point in the pre-human-to-modern-human process, the outcome *could* have been very different. Looking at the evolutionary process backwards through time gives a false sense of inevitability—what happened is what was *supposed* to happen. On the other hand, biologists know that evolution builds on what's already present. It doesn't, for example, produce an entirely different kind of brain with each new species that emerges in a particular animal line. Rather than wrangling with the kinds of word-game arguments creationism poses, it's more helpful to look at what we actually know.

We most certainly evolved from the archaic humans who came before us and they, in turn, evolved from the Hominini clade that separated from other primates two million years ago. It's true that our unique arrangement of intelligence, cognitive fluency, and self-awareness is the result of trends that originated in those other beings, but it's also true that we can never know if our "unique" arrangement was inevitable. I believe it was, but I recognize this is a theological argument, not a scientific one.

The biologist part of my brain assures me there's not a shred of evidence to support my theological claim. It's entirely possible that our archaic ancestors could have continued as they were for tens of thousands of years, and then slowly died off or, just as likely, have given rise to new Homo species similar to us but not us. Great evolutionary biologists like Stephen J. Gould, George Gaylord Simpson, and Ernst Mayr have identified trends within the evolutionary process that help us conceptualize it in rational and predictive ways. But it's impossible to look at a single species and say that its existence was inevitable or entirely accidental. Biology can't answer such questions.

As Francisca Cho reminds us, we must be cautious that our use of language doesn't cloud our perception of what's actually there. The phenomenon of evolution is what it is, and it's not required to conform to our convenient "either/or" concepts like inevitability versus accident. I believe our existence was inevitable on *theological* grounds—as a way of bringing meaning into the universe—but I recognize the philosophical limitations of this reasoning too.

All we can say for certain is that we exist, and our profoundly unique minds seem to be telling us that there's much more going on out there than can be seen through a scientific lens. This doesn't mean we should ignore what science is telling us, particularly about our own remarkable story. It's significant that Neanderthals populated the outside-Africa world long before we did because they, like us, made tools, cooked with fire, built stone monuments, wore clothes, buried their dead. They probably spoke simple languages. They cooperated to hunt, gather food, and protect their tribes. Their gradual disappearance from the world, from about twenty to sixty thousand years ago, coincided with the steady incursion of modern humans into their habitats. Their demise has been attributed to violence from modern humans but also assimilation (most of us carry some Neanderthal genes), as well as disease and climate change. It was likely a combination of those things, but these are just secondary to the real, underlying reason: Neanderthals were *unlike* us in one crucial detail. They weren't capable of acquiring, refining, and passing along information the way we can. They lacked our evolutionarily unique cognitive capacity, our cognitive "fluidity," which is why human civilization and not Neanderthal tribes now dominate the habitable face of the planet.[8,9]

The Emergence of Art

Put aside the scientific narrative of human evolution and consider a theological narrative. In Alone in the World, the theological anthropologist J. Wentzel Van Huyssteen explores the German theologian Wolfhart Pannenberg's idea that human uniqueness is rooted in our "exocentricity"—our intrinsic urge to look beyond our immediate physical world and become something more than our immediate selves. We have an "openness" to the world like no animal before us.[10] We possess a different sense of being in the world than other animals, which includes our distant archaic human cousins. We're unrestricted by any one environment; we're globally adaptable and gazing at the stars. Our story as living beings on Earth is undeniably unique. As Francisca Cho's Buddhist analysis might suggest, when a theological narrative offers an insight that's as equally and intuitively satisfying as a parallel scientific insight, on what grounds do we so readily dismiss it? Why must one be true and the other false?

Pannenberg suggested that this openness to the world, this *weltoffenheit*, is also what marks us as uniquely "made in God's image." Our exocentricity compels us to seek beyond who we are and become more than we are. Individually and as a species we're in a constant state of becoming which Pannenberg interpreted as an urge for unity with God.

Setting aside references to God, I believe this theological framing of human uniqueness outshines any scientific explanation for the emergence of art. In the archeological record, nothing sets us apart from our distant ancestors more convincingly than artifactual and pictorial expressions of perceptions from within the psyche. As Catholic writer Tina Beattie points out, the earliest art humans brought into the world spoke to an awakening of religious imagination and transcendence.[11] Anatomically modern humans looked at the same world as their archaic human ancestors but saw something different: something that had a story and meaning.

Current theories suggest that humans possessed the cognitive and imaginative capacity for art long before they started expressing it. What caused the first artistic stirrings to emerge is still in dispute, but as anatomically modern humans gained ground and their settlements became more established there was a gradual blossoming of artifacts, carvings and engravings that served no pragmatic or survival purpose other than as expressions of emotional and imaginative awakening. It seems to have begun in Africa and spread from there throughout the nascent human world. Some scientists attribute this eruption of highly evolved and imaginative behavior to a fine tuning of the human genome that happened when groups of early humans became more settled and secure. We can't retroactively know which minor genetic changes occurred nor how they influenced intelligence and cognitive ability. What's known is that this "upper paleolithic revolution" heralded the emergence of a mind unlike any other, with unprecedented and unique degrees of worldly perception, social intuition, and inner reflection. The artifacts left by this ancient but anatomically modern human mind blended spiritual insight, awareness of mortality, and fascination with nature's rhythms. It was a mind that could conceive of an existence beyond mortal existence, a transcendent reality. A mind that brought meaning into the world.[12]

From what these first Homo sapiens *sapiens* (our true species name) left behind, we know little or nothing of their conception of God, gods, or transcendent worlds. But we can say that religious ideation seems to have co-emerged with the unique cognitive and intellectual abilities that distinguished them not just from other archaic humans but from all other animals.

Perhaps the most distinctive early remnants of this cultural-metaphysical revolution were the cave paintings created fifteen to twenty thousand years ago. The best preserved and most elaborate examples are those in southern Europe, but humans created similar works in many other parts of the world they inhabited at that time. They were expressions of a mind that could now fully separate itself from its environment, observe it, reimagine it, and imbue it with meaning. We can immediately recognize the intelligence and aesthetic mastery embodied in these works. The juxtaposition of animal and human forms suggests a deliberate arrangement intended to tell a story. Multidisciplinary analysis of one of the most significant examples of cave art, the Lascaux cave, suggests intertwining themes such as the fertility cycles of the animals depicted, the passage of time, and awareness of transcendent forces behind physical reality.[13] Our modern minds can readily appreciate how skillfully, with simple lines and shading, the creators captured the essence of their subjects. Their sophistication indicates the same level of self-critique and dedication to craft as any contemporary artist. Even if it can't be scientifically proven, it's clear that these prehistoric artists sought to engage the aesthetic sense of the viewer. We recognize symbolic reasoning and a mind like our own reflecting back at us from prehistory.

Some scholars suggest the paintings were meant to portray a higher reality reflected in our earthly reality, and that the murals were meant to transform the interior space of the cave into a link between the natural and supernatural worlds. The artists may have also believed they achieved divine grace through the very act of creating the paintings, not unlike the unknown artisans and laborers who built the magnificent cathedrals of the European Middle Ages.

We can't know the motives behind these works of art, but we do know that the effort needed to produce them (many of them required extensive planning and shared labor to build scaffolding and refine pigments, among other things) demonstrates a collective willingness to expend precious resources to give form and substance to abstract beliefs and concepts. Nor do we know how late Paleolithic people incorporated religious and spiritual beliefs into their day to day lives.

The World as Divine Substance

Humans found an alternative way of memorializing their thoughts and expressing transcendent feelings with the invention of written language about five to six thousand years ago. In a sense, symbolic language could transpose the inner pictorial space of the cave to the reader's mind. This monumental event marked the boundary of prehistoric and historical time. It has allowed us, their distant descendants, to directly know what they were thinking. Written records allow scholars to contrast the stated beliefs of ancient civilizations with the objective, historic record of what is known about their lives. We can track how religious ideas and expectations influenced and were influenced by the ebb and flow of social change, economics, and politics.

Not surprisingly, the first religious ideas put into writing seem rooted in beliefs established in preliterate times. Despite cultural and geographic differences, they show a remarkable affinity for the idea that the earth and its people were born from the bodies of fallen gods, or were created by gods from cosmic substance.[14] (How coincidentally close to the modern scientific creation story!) Early Sanskrit tablets describe the Hindu god Vishnu dreaming the world into existence.[15] Such narratives speak to an ancient, deeply grounded, and widespread understanding that humans were somehow the physical embodiments of divine substance and the world is an incarnation of a sacred reality.

The preliterate roots of these ideas about the earth's creation can't be traced, but it's fascinating that many tribal societies in the south Pacific and Americas which we consider similar to Neolithic societies seem to have held similar views prior to their contact with Westerners. It's also fascinating that ancient people and many contemporary tribal societies base their moral views on the belief that human nature reflects divine nature. Through worship and practice, people could reinforce this divine connection or fill themselves with mana or divine spirit.[16] The world order, the earthly cycles of time and nature, reflected the perfect order of divine reality. Human religious codes were intended to reflect this higher order. Kings and political leaders imposed rules of conduct intended to maintain order, but the gods themselves weren't necessarily keeping track of people's behavior. As religious historian and writer Karen Armstrong explained in *A History of God*, ancient divine beings of creation mythology seldom involved themselves directly in the profane lives of humans.[17]

But this relationship between human and divine grew more nuanced in the developing beliefs of the Semitic people who became the ancient Israelites, during the period of 1-1000 BCE, when the Old Testament was written. As Armstrong noted, Biblical texts allude to humans and God being made of *different* substance.[18] The Bible never wavers on that distinction, but from earlier to later Biblical periods God becomes more directly personal and engaged in real-world events. This important social and intellectual shift in religious worldview was incorporated into the two other great monotheisms, Christianity and Islam, that emerged from Judaism. The question of whether humans are made of divine substance or if God is wholly other-than-human has echoed down through modern times and remains with us today.

Twilight of the Gods?

Some psychologists and social scientists who study religion would see this crucial metaphysical question of God's nature as a tempest in a teapot because both claims are merely examples of religious memes—ideas that resonate with human modes of thinking and behavior. Memes don't need to be true or valid as long as they're emotionally satisfying and serve some cultural or social purpose.[19] Pondering whether gods and humans are made of the same substance helps enrich people's religious experience. The fact that there is no God and it's therefore a meaningless question is beside the point. It's a question that's survived for thousands of years because it served a valuable cultural purpose.

After looking at the history of its psychosocial origins we might assume that religious belief is a natural expression of emerging human self-awareness and insight. But we'd be wrong, say these atheist cognitive scientists and psychologists. Religious belief isn't an inevitable and permanent feature of the human mind, they'd say. Religion's "naturalness" is an illusion or, in the words of one such scientist, Richard Dawkins, a "God delusion."[20] Religious beliefs helped groups of prehistoric humans cope with environmental challenges. Today's religions are assemblages of memes that have been repackaged and passed along through human cultures. But just because they helped earlier people cope with their natural and social environments doesn't mean we need to hang onto them, says Dawkins, and we'd all be better off without them.

Psychologist Daniel Dennett argues that religious memes originated from our instinctive urge to detect unseen "agents" who cause things to happen.[21] When something goes bump in the night, we want to know who made the noise. Ancient people wanted to know who or what agent made good things and bad things happen to them. When no worldly agents could be detected, they invented invisible, purposeful agents at work in nature.[22]

Agency detection theory is the conceptual framework for a coalition of cognitive scientists, psychologists, and philosophers who study religion from an uncompromisingly atheist perspective. They might agree that no scientific specialty can fully explain religious belief right now. But ultimately there's no aspect of religion that can't be explained in terms of cognitive miscues and emotional reasoning.

This school of thought says our urge to detect invisible agents at work in nature is rooted in a cognitive phenomenon known as Theory of Mind. Humans acquire Theory of Mind in early childhood as they begin to grasp: "I have a mind that's separate from my body. It's the part of me that feels and thinks and makes plans... but other people also have minds that feel and think and make plans."[23] As children mature they become more adept at using Theory of Mind to help them interpret other people's thoughts and motives. It becomes deeply integrated into day-to-day thinking. It helps them develop strategies for forming relationships and maneuvering the social environment. But it becomes so second nature to us that we also tend to project it onto inanimate objects and natural forces. When we make the weather gods angry, they make it rain on our parade.

It's easy to see how people in both the recent and distant past attributed motives and personalities to invisible minds at work in nature. Spirits who directed the wind and controlled the sun could use their powers to punish the guilty and reward the innocent. Fear of punishment from an invisible, all knowing deity helped impose self-discipline on tribe members and reinforced humans' innate social tendency for altruistic behavior. It discouraged cheating—stealing food or mates—and gave tribal leaders a basis for enforcing behavioral codes. It may have also favored certain genetically based behavioral tendencies. People who were more innately inclined to conform to moral codes and social constraints were more likely to reproduce and pass their tendencies along to their offspring.[24]

Cognitive scientist Pascal Boyer argues that besides aligning with our natural urge for agency detection, religious ideas tend to be counterintuitive—they stick with us because they involve explanations outside the realm of usual experience.[25] If we believe the wind caused a tree to make an unusual sound, we soon dismiss the experience from our thoughts because the wind whistling through trees happens all the time. But if we believe an evil spirit caused the unusual sound, we commit mental resources of memory and meaning to the experience. Stories about burning bushes or bleeding statues hold our attention. When understood from this vantage point, says Boyer, we see that religious ideas are "parasitic," in that they stir the imagination and kidnap mental resources designed for other, more important adaptive purposes.[26]

Our sophisticated cognitive abilities bestowed us with biologically unprecedented adaptive advantages, Boyer continues, but this came with a cost. Other intelligent animals seek agency in environmental cues, but our agency detection is deeply entwined with our social intelligence which causes us to perceive the world in shades of meaning, intention, and volition, particularly when faced with phenomenon that threaten us or don't align with expectations. This explains why religion is such a deeply imbedded feature of human existence, says Boyer. Our sophisticated imaginative ability, which normally allows us to project and calculate future events, also motivates us to assemble a patchwork of religious ideas that account for the bewildering complexity of the universe and the frightening realities of existence, such as mortality. Our intelligence requires explanations, and religion provides them and gives us assurance that what may not make sense to us nevertheless makes sense to a deity. Religious explanations make our mortality more bearable and provide a basis for powerful, socially binding rituals, ideologies, and rules of behavior that are easily transmittable and adaptable to cultural changes.[27, 28]

Atheist Shadows on Academic Walls

This sounds very convincing, and many social scientists now routinely approach their work with a presumption that the agency theory of religion is important for understanding basic social dynamics. A 2014 study of the religious practices of 583 contemporary tribal societies, each with its own cultural history and language or dialect, claimed to show that social and environmental stress can increase belief in "moralizing high gods"—social science research jargon for deities who observe, judge, and respond to human behaviors. The study's five authors, from top tier research institutes and universities in Australia, Canada, New Zealand, and the US, said that despite the tribes' cultural diversity and global distribution—from the American West to central Africa and Eastern Europe—they showed the same link between faith in a judgmental deity, social stability, and material success. The authors concluded that "a shared belief in moralizing high gods can improve a group's ability to deal with environmental duress and may therefore be ecologically adaptive."[29]

The authors suggested that ancient humans faced the same sort of impoverishment and environmental challenges as the groups they studied. Therefore, belief in the presence of a watchful and judgmental deity probably played a crucial role in the development of Neolithic societies.

But another study of 414 societies, published by thirteen scientists at universities in Austria, Germany, Ireland, Japan, the UK, and the US, showed that "belief in morally concerned supernatural agents" was *not* a prerequisite for "the evolution of social complexity" and, in fact, belief in intrusive and judgmental gods might only occur in relatively complex, multiethnic megasocieties of more than a million people.[30]

The fact that these two equally impressive studies seem to contradict each other demonstrates the hazards of analyzing human society through the lens of a theory based on dubious and simplistic assumptions about human religiosity. Most religious traditions integrate divine judgment and punishment into their behavioral codes and worldviews. But to assume that these ideas provide the psychological framework of all religious belief is just flat out wrong and speaks to an atheistic bias that amounts to theological illiteracy on the part of highly educated people who should know better.

Besides the limits of agency-punishment theory to explain anything,[31] its critics also question the value of comparing modern tribal communities to Neolithic societies. Just because a group of humans can sustain themselves in the wild with no modern resources doesn't make them similar to groups of humans who lived tens of thousands of years ago. Modern tribes may have remained 'uncontaminated' and insulated from the outside world due to cultural practices that make them very different from pre-historic humans.

And while no one can deny fear of punishment as a recurring feature of many religions, it's also true that Western secular societies have found ways to induce group cooperation without reference to supernatural punishment or divine intervention. Conversely, some successful religions lack any reference to these ideas.

Critics of these kinds of studies say that agency-punisher god theories might provide *some* insights of how religion took hold and flourished in early human societies. They might demonstrate how a shared set of religious beliefs contributes to social stability—the formative role religion played in the advancement of human civilization. But didn't we already know that? So what's their *real* motive for retracing old ground with this new cognitive-psychosocial theory?

The Hubris of Atheistic Bias

By explaining religion through the lens of agency and punishment theory, we're subtly invited to regard religion as a kind of social disease to be cured; a problem to be solved. In other words: we've deconstructed religion under the cognitive theory microscope and identified the glitch in the operating system. Now, having identified the cognitive coding error, we can perhaps cure the world of religion and make it go away. But, as many other scientists and scholars who study religion have observed, exposing the cognitive flaws imbedded within religious belief won't make it go away because the neuropsychological roots of religion extend beyond the framework of cognitive science. Agency and punishment theory is inherently atheistic. It makes no room for the possible authenticity of religious belief. By showing how it can account for human religiosity its proponents subtly invite us to share their atheism. As critics point out, this becomes evident when agency and punishment theorists shift their focus from the religious beliefs of marginal and unfamiliar indigenous tribal groups to those of established global religions. For example, in *Religion Explained,* Boyer touts his approach as the best and most insightful way for explaining why Catholics gather in a "special building" to hear the retelling of an ancient tale of torture and crucifixion and, when the story is finished, "pretend to eat the flesh of a god."[32]

While it's correct that Eastertime Gospel readings refer to Christ's crucifixion, they're not part of routine practice, despite the entertainment industry's lurid depictions of torture and horror as synonymous with Catholicism. Most Catholics would consider Boyer's description of Catholic ritual to be cartoonish, offensive, and unrecognizable, as would Protestants, Jews, and Muslims if he made similar references to their practices. By shading his ideas with disrespectful cultural tropes he exposes his own very unscientific biases. Yes, a church is a "special building," but so is a post office or a Starbucks. And I'm sure many and perhaps most Catholics would say they attend mass not out of guilt or fear but to quiet their minds, rejuvenate their spirits, and focus their attention on reconnecting with God and themselves in the presence of an accepting, open community; they enter the "special building" to find temporary refuge from an anxious, materialistic world; they "pretend" to eat the flesh of God because the intense yet contemplative moment associated with "pretending" (a.k.a. communion) helps them consciously achieve (sometimes, but not always) a felt experience of God, or the "experience of the numinous" to use theologian Paul Tillich's words.[33] The Vietnamese monk and Buddhist scholar Thich Nhat Hanh grasped the deep spiritual significance of the Christian Eucharist and likened it to a burst of mindfulness through which we can touch the cosmos.[34]

Moreover, I believe most Catholics and practitioners of other faiths are perfectly capable of understanding Boyer's agency theory as well as Dennett's and Dawkins's atheistic arguments. In reading their words one gets the impression they presume that only the academic elite can truly appreciate their invaluable scientific insights. In fact, their ideas are really not that complicated. As religious writer Karen Armstrong and other critics have said, atheists like Boyer and Dennett demean their own otherwise valuable ideas by implying that religious people don't understand why they do the things they do, and only psychologists, anthropologists, and other scholars are capable of discerning their real motives.[35] This approach conflates religious belief with physical or mental illness: the patient might think they know what's wrong, but only a highly trained professional can identify the root of the problem.

I believe most religious practitioners would agree there are aspects of agency theory that make sense. We all tend to infer invisible agents afoot in the world when things go in our favor or work against us. And no one can deny that thoughts of reward or punishment in the afterlife—if there is an afterlife—are a widespread and deeply ingrained feature of human civilization. But are these the things that compel most people to practice their faiths? I believe most practitioners of major world religions would say, regardless of their views on the afterlife, that they participate in religious ceremonies not from fear but mainly to experience joy, connection, and a wide range of deep feelings that are too complex and nuanced to express. They're into religion more for its immediacy than for its afterlife potential. It's fine for public intellectuals like Boyer, Dawkins, and Dennett to publish their own ideas about religious beliefs, but it's troubling to see these theories being cemented into the academic establishment through the steady increase of agency and punishment theory studies being published in peer-reviewed research journals.

The Limits of Reductionism

Many scholars and writers who concern themselves with religion remind us that connecting cognitive and mental phenomenon with the biological substrate of the mind remains a daunting scientific challenge. When cognitive theorists and psychologists speak of "memes" and "mental modules" or "inputs" and "outputs," it's crucial to remember and oh-so-tempting to forget that they're using twenty-first century tech speak to describe biophysical processes occurring within an eighty-six-billion-neuron biosystem with a three-and-a-half-billion-year phylogenic legacy. The human brain is profoundly more complex than the words and concepts available to us to describe it. We might derive some useful insights by deconstructing the conscious mind as if it were a computer with apps and an operating system. But insights and clues shouldn't be confused with conclusive understanding, which is far beyond the horizon of current science. For example, while cognitive scientists downplay the importance of the unconscious mind in mental processing, psychiatrists and clinical psychologists believe it plays a crucial role in human behavior.[36] The boundaries of the unconscious remain undefined; it's the repository of memories, dreams, and primordial feelings, and the entryway of neurosensory information. The fact that computers don't have biologically evolved unconscious minds should remind us of their limited utility as models of human intelligence and consciousness. It's not that cognitive science doesn't have something useful to say about religion, but by no means should it have the *only* say.

Cracks in the Atheist Foundation

Within the framework of cognitive theory of religion, Rutgers University professor of psychology and religion James Jones says the atheistic arguments of Boyer, Dennett, and Dawkins exaggerate the influence of lower level cognitive operations on upper level conscious thoughts and feelings.[37] Studies from a range of different neuroscience and neuropsychological specialties show that religious ideas engage multiple levels of conscious awareness. As neuroimaging studies have shown, contemplating God and spiritual ideas seems to arise from many different parts of the brain to synergistically produce a holistic awareness which one neuroscientist described as Absolute Unity of Being.[38] What religious debunkers are seeking to do is sift all this down to a simple, mechanical model in which higher levels of religious awareness are entirely determined by lower cognitive operations, says Jones. The flaw in their model is that it views the flow of control as entirely one-way, from bottom to top.[39] All higher-level conscious thoughts are reducible to lower-level cognitive operations. But this goes far beyond what the evidence of cognitive science research actually says, Jones explains.

The religious debunkers' bottom-to-top model is contradicted by findings derived from scientific studies outside cognitive science, such as clinical psychological evidence demonstrating the importance of top-to-bottom causation in which conscious thoughts influence underlying neuronal and physiological processes.[40] For example, says Jones, the clinical field of psychoneuroimmunology is based on observations that a person's conscious psychological processes can directly influence their immune system, endocrine system, and other essential physiological systems.[41] What we "think" can literally change our physiological chemistry. Health providers have long known that mindfulness meditation can have measurable and sustained positive health benefits.

The brain mechanisms behind these examples of top-down influence of mind over body aren't clear, says Jones, but the evidence nonetheless presents scientists who believe in strict, mechanistic cognitive control over conscious awareness with the unsettling fact that the mind can overrule the influence of cognitive memes.[42] They might influence how we perceive and understand the world, but they're just one thread of a matrix that remains largely hidden from us. Jones's insights align with neuroimaging data showing how meditation, spiritual contemplation, and belief in God can influence physical brain structure. No doubt some aspects of religious awareness can be attributed to cognitive memes, but it's a narrow lens with which to view a vast neurological and psychological cosmos.

Religious Experience as Ineffable Truth

Rather than seeing agency detection as the basis for the origins of religion, an alternative view holds that religion arose when the pre-human mind acquired the capacity to detach itself from immediate experience and perceive its own being. Returning to Van Huyssteen's and Pannenberg's idea of *Imago Dei*, we became the world's first religious beings when our subsistence-focused animal minds gradually transformed into exocentric minds looking beyond ourselves to become something more.

This open-to-the-world, self-aware mind was inexorably drawn to use its problem-solving skills to ponder metaphysical questions about life, existence, and the universe. It experienced wonder when it gazed up at the stars and transcendent joy from gathering around a fire with loving family and friends. Contrary to cognitive science theory, this ancient human mind didn't require invisible agents to help explain sensations of joy, mystery, and wonder any more than we do. Such feelings by themselves can become the basis of religious belief as we integrate them with our unique experiences and imaginations.

The human mind experiences and understands the world in "biologically unprecedented" ways,[43] says van Huyssteen, who specializes in the interface of science and religion, particularly on the emergence of religion as expressed in neolithic art.

Van Huyssteen argues that science and theology have reached a point where they must collaborate to advance our understanding of human spirituality and religious behavior. Science alone isn't equipped to deal with the subjective, intuitive, and symbolic dimensions of religious experience. The cognitive and perceptive abilities that give rise to religious awareness and that make religious belief so powerful for us transcend the scope of psychology and so they can't be entirely explained in terms of other psychological operations.[44] But just as scientists must accept these limitations, theologians must accept that evolution is the "unavoidable tool" God used to create humanity,[45] says van Huyssteen. Modern religion must reconcile itself with anthropological truth. Humans are deeply and unavoidably rooted in nature. Like it or not, religious believers must come to accept that the facts of human evolution and the biological underpinnings of human thought can't be disputed.

As we'll see, humanity's enduring need for religious experience is embedded deep within our psyches and can't be attributed to only cultural influences or tribal instincts. Purely objective, scientific explanations of the origins of religion that are themselves void of any religious or subjective insight, such as agency and punishment theory of cognitive science, will only ever be one-dimensional and unsatisfactory. Neither anthropology nor neuroscience alone can adequately explain religion or religious experience. And neither discipline can explain the "internal rationality of religious belief," van Huyssteen adds. Only a religious person practicing their faith within a specific cultural context can say if a particular experience is a religious experience.[46]

As Tina Beattie argues, every person's unique imagination plays a legitimate and vital role in how they experience religion. How else would we make religious feelings and insights relevant to our own lives?

Science-based atheism would be correct in denying the authenticity of religious belief if imagination were its only component, but it's not. Imagination helps us individually process and derive meaning from the psychological tendencies that drive religious belief, which science has now shown we all share. Because subjective experience and imagination can't be objectified and standardized, science naturally seeks to minimize their importance. But that doesn't mean they're not important.

Consider imagination from an artistic context. Few scientists would deny the legitimacy of art and its obvious value for expressing feelings and seeing the world in a way that's profoundly different from the scientific perspective but often more meaningful and insightful. Psychologists might describe the mental processes behind the aesthetic urge, but we all know that nothing comes close to hearing the words of the artists themselves. No one would deny the authenticity of an artist's own insights. Psychological analysis might provide a *different* understanding of those insights, but not necessarily a better one. The same holds true for religious experience. Without the guidance of religious practitioners and a theological perspective to help navigate the imaginative inner world of religious experience, science is limited in what it can learn about the psychology and neurobiology of religious belief. There's a "naturalness" to human religious imagination, says Van Huyssteen, an embeddedness that challenges any scientific attempt to marginalize it as merely a product of human culture.[47]

Because science speaks the language of reductionism—explaining physical events in terms of underlying processes—it struggles to adequately explain a conscious event that, like consciousness itself, has a quality that can't be found in its component parts, just as a symphony's ineffable beauty would be lost if the musicians played their parts in sequence rather than together. Religious awareness can't be deconstructed the way science wants to deconstruct it.

Summarizing the insights of many colleagues dedicated to understanding theological anthropology, Van Huyssteen makes the case that science must take a more enlightened and open-minded approach to the subject of how people use their imaginative abilities to create a cultural framework for religious belief and communication. Just because we use our imaginations and symbolic reasoning to help formulate religious ideas doesn't mean the root source of the ideas is imaginary. A perceived inner truth expressed imaginatively and symbolically is still a truth. It's entirely possible, he suggests, that the vast neural complexity of the human mind has given us the capacity to perceive things and be aware of aspects of reality that exceed the biological nature of the brain.[48] These perceptions can only be interpreted and expressed in imaginative ways. In other words, it's entirely reasonable and rational that conventional science, which can only deal with physical reality, is approaching the limits of what it can tell us about ourselves and our existence. How is this so?

Cognitive Fluidity: How We Make Meaning

Heightened self-awareness—awareness of oneself as a free-thinking being simultaneously separate but connected to other beings—was one of the distinguishing features of our distant human ancestors who emerged from Africa. Artifactual evidence suggests that modern humanity's emotionally and symbolically rich religious behaviors first appeared alongside this heightened awareness.[49]

Self-awareness is a hallmark of higher order animal consciousness. It implies an awareness of one's mental processes occurring internally and separately from the world, as Theory of Mind suggests. But human self-awareness is coupled to an intelligence and cognitive virtuosity unseen in any other animal, which makes our awareness of being "detached from the world yet engaged with the world" deep and complex. Not only are our brains genetically endowed with the neural capacity for sophisticated cognitive operations, as are other intelligent animals, but unlike other animals we're also endowed with the ability to instantly and fluidly integrate cognitive activities. Thoughts and information can simultaneously flow through multiple cognitive operations such as reasoning, remembering, emotional processing, evaluating, and imagining.[50]

Moreover, beyond our conscious awareness, our unconscious minds also seem capable of similar high-level cognitive processing. Our advanced cognitive abilities come so naturally to us that we often don't appreciate how unique we are. Some scholars have suggested this "cognitive fluidity" is the biological counterpart to *Imago Dei*—humans made in God's image—which implies humanity's spiritual uniqueness in the world.

Human cognitive fluidity means unconscious insights can be integrated with conscious insights and imaginative reasoning to produce religious ideologies. Social awareness and practical reasoning can produce systems of morality. When the national media broadcasted images of refugee families detained in prisons on the Mexican border under the Trump administration's immigration policy, many Christian communities were at the forefront of denouncing the policy, making the intuitive connection between the refugee's plight and their own religious duty to care for the poor and marginalized. Some congregations replaced their church Christmas creches with scenes depicting imprisoned children separated from their imprisoned parents, drawing a parallel between refugee families and the nativity story of Mary and Joseph returning from Egypt, poor, oppressed, and threatened by authorities.

Unlike any beings before us, our unique cognitive processing causes us to perceive the world holistically and infuse it with meaning. We don't just possess *more* intelligence than other animals; we possess a *different kind* of intelligence. Some scientists and theologians describe this as "epiphenomenal" awareness of the world,[51] an awareness that evolved from biological origins for biological purposes but which now transcends any biological or adaptive purpose. Epiphenomenal awareness opens us to something beyond the immediate, inferred reality in which our biological brains routinely dwell—a higher level apprehension or recognition of something that precedes all other experience. Though shaped by evolution, epiphenomenal awareness is hyper-biological, grounded in nature but capable of transcending nature. It offers another way—a more biological and less theological way perhaps—to understand Pannenberg's *weltoffenheit,* our uniquely human openness to the world.

Although most humans now live in manufactured environments, cognitive scientists can show that we still use our minds for adaptive and survival purposes, as humans always have. We share with other intelligent animals the same immediate awareness of our environments. This is the dimension of awareness within which cognitive scientists want to "explain" human religion. But we're also aware of ourselves as mortal beings in an infinite universe. This epiphenomenal awareness empowers us to use our minds in ways with no discernable biologic purpose, such as art and religion. The cognitive approach to explaining religion shows how *some* aspects of religious belief can be attributed to agency and imagination—invisible agents cause things to happen and we imagine we can know who those agents are and why they do what they do. But this is just a narrow band of the broad spectrum of religious awareness. The human propensity for religious behavior and religious experience speaks to something more fundamental and profound taking place in our minds than can be fully captured by a scientific theory, no matter how elegantly crafted it is.

It must have been epiphenomenal awareness, *weltoffenheit,* that inspired the ancient and beautiful Hindu creation story of the god Vishnu dreaming the universe into existence while floating on the cosmic river of time. This magical vision seeks to organize the epiphenomenon of a timeless universe into a meaningful whole. Contrast this ancient story with the theory recently proposed by cosmologists and physicists at Canada's Perimeter Institute, which is rapidly gaining ground, that says our four-dimensional spacetime universe is a hologram of a higher dimensional universe projected through the event horizon of a black hole. I'm sure the authors would claim that rational scientific inquiry led them to their theory. But it is epiphenomenal awareness of a universe in need of explaining that drives this grand level of scientific inquiry.

I love that both these cosmic visions explain the limits of human perception in much the same way. Because we're brought into existence by Vishnu's dream, we can only see inside the dream and not what's beyond it. And, according to the holographic universe theory, because our brains evolved in a four-dimensional reality, we're incapable of seeing the higher dimensional reality that brought us to life.

Science and Religion are Mysteries to Each Other

Some authors suggest human uniqueness, or *Imago Dei*, represents a state of "singularity" between two complementary perceptions of reality: the heightened awareness from which religious sensibility emerges and the scientific reality that the human mind emerged from nature and therefore can't transcend the laws of nature. Neuroscientists might eventually be able to describe how the biophysics of heightened epiphenomenal awareness differ from other mental states which could help support claims that religious perceptions are authentic and not imagined. Already there's evidence that for many religious practitioners the reality they experience through religious awareness seems more "real" to them than the day-to-day physical reality our biological brains were designed to perceive.[53] Looking from the outside in, neuroscientists may be able to describe how religious experience appears to activate certain neuron fields and circuits. They may be able to explain why religious awareness affects other aspects of human health and behavior. But the core epiphenomenal mystery of religious awareness will probably always be elusive. Like their quantum physicist colleagues, neuroscientists, evolutionary psychologists, and others who study the biology and psychology of religious belief must learn to live with a phenomenon that they can describe theoretically but never fully explain.

And, equally, theologians and religious practitioners must address the distant evolutionary origins of our religious reasoning, as Van Huyssteen suggests.[54] Coming to terms with evolution is no longer just a question of adapting religious creation myths to align with biological history. It's about accepting that the human mind was shaped by biological evolution to be a religious mind. Prophetic and revelatory events that marked new eras of religious awareness occurred within this context. Humanity didn't suddenly awaken to one religious revelation or another; we continuously awaken to new insights and meaning. As Larycia Hawkins alluded to in her Facebook event, we all emerged from the same primordial clay with the same capacity for religious belief and experience.

This poses an ideological challenge for religious practitioners who believe their version of religious truth is the only truth. But perhaps there's consolation in knowing that a deeper, more nuanced understanding of evolution can provide religious leaders a deeper and more nuanced understanding of the behavior of the people they lead.

For example, competition is far less important in the story of human existence than altruism and cooperation. Yet, as evolutionary biologist Joan Roughgarden points out, the evolutionary principle of "survival of the fittest," which refers to gradual genetic change within a species, is frequently invoked to justify destructive behaviors at all levels of society under the completely bogus claim that this somehow relates to natural law. It doesn't, says Roughgarden, it relates to Social Darwinism, a pseudoscience distortion of actual Darwinism which grossly oversimplifies evolutionary dynamics.[55]

It's fascinating that monotheism's core values of charity, empathy, and respect for human dignity so closely align with our bio-social heritage. Evolutionary psychology wants us to believe that they're more than aligned—they're the *same*. But they're not. The nuanced difference between scientific altruism and religious altruism is all the difference in the world. Evolutionary psychology claims that if we strip away the doctrines, myths, and symbolism, we'll reveal the psychic clockwork of evolution's most sophisticated social animal—but an *animal* nonetheless. Theologians have disputed this claim, which is why it's crucial for religious opinion leaders and theologians to engage in the evolutionary psychology debate. Christian, Islamic, and Judaic beliefs relating to human dignity may have emerged from bio-psychic roots, but emergent qualities are different from the substrate they emerged from. The evolutionary and cognitive science versions of altruism say that humans suppressing their individual desires to help other humans in the group allowed the entire group to adapt and thrive, which is absolutely correct: it enabled an efficient division of labor; it allowed the group to conserve resources; it decreased destructive conflicts. This scientific version of the story says that the first traces of religious belief emerged when humans adapted their innate biases and cognitive mistakes to promote altruistic behaviors. An invisible spirit is watching to see if you play by the rules, including your behavior towards others, and will reward or punish you in this life or the next.

And, in fact, much of what passes for religious behavior today does echo this distant reasoning. How often do we hear people of faith attribute their material success in this life to their acts of charity, as if God has rewarded their altruism? Or, confidently proclaim that their charitable work in this world has procured a better deal in the next?

But many religious writers and theologians would point to the doctrinal fallacy in this reasoning. The Bible and Gospels make no guarantees about altruistic behavior. Some "good" people are rewarded; some know only suffering. What most contemporary theologians and religious writers would say is that Christian, Islamic, and Judaic doctrines stress that charitable deeds, the honoring of human dignity, are their own reward. There's no implied bargain or negotiation. We see in the eyes and face of other humans the eyes and face of humans made in God's image. Their suffering is our suffering, and we alleviate it because that's what humans made in God's image do. We rise above the social animal described by cognitive science and evolutionary psychology and become fully human.

What I'm saying was expressed far more eloquently by the Jewish theologian Abraham Heschel: humans—made of dust and ashes—become holy by performing God's mitsvots—by loving their neighbors as themselves, by not hating, killing, stealing, cheating. We rise beyond our animal nature to our uniquely human nature when we bring God's will into the world.[56]

Religion illuminates precisely what science cannot, said Heschel—the qualities of human nature that are beyond the scope of science. This is religion's purpose, and this is precisely what's being lost in the scientific (and cultural) effort to deconstruct religion in psycho-social terms. Rather than asking what connects us to the animal world we should be seeking what sets us apart.[57]

I believe theologians and religious writers are best equipped to explain what sets us apart, but they themselves can only participate in the debate if they understand evolutionary science. As Van Huyssteen correctly points out: Theologians can ignore science, but who would listen to them?[58] If theologians and religious practitioners want to help write new narratives of meaning and faith to avert the self-destructive trajectory we seem to be on, they must be able to see the world through a biological lens.

4

Stardust and Mud

The final scene of the 2013 film *Gravity* punctuates the story's deeply spiritual theme with an allusion to human evolution. The astronaut played by Sandra Bullock struggles to escape a reentry capsule that's plummeted to the bottom of a lake. As she tears at the waterlogged space suit tethering her to the capsule a frog passes by, kicking its way to the surface for a breath of air. Finally freeing herself, she too rises to the surface and gasps a life-saving breath. Near exhaustion, she thrashes her way to the shore and collapses on the muddy bank, motionless. Slowly then, she pushes herself up from the mud, crawling, struggling, rising to her knees, head bent to the ground and, finally, lifting herself upright, moving forward, footprints in the mud, eyes facing the horizon.

The film, a remarkable narrative of metaphysical death and rebirth, received the high praise it deserved. But critics who panned it did so not for its lack of usual space movie fare (aliens, heroes, choreographed violence, time warps) but because of its poignant depiction of human frailty and mortality in an unfathomable environment in which we didn't evolve and (my bias) in which we have no real reason to be. Although the story takes place in space stations orbiting the earth, space is just the malevolent backdrop for a humanistic tale of spiritual enlightenment. Adrift in orbit around a wondrous blue Earth, Bullock's astronaut is also adrift emotionally over the death of her child years earlier. She survives a disaster caused by an errant satellite only by embracing the reality of her own death and surrendering to the earthly embrace of gravity. Not your typical Hollywood space drama.

Her descent through the atmosphere, her struggle to escape the womb of the sunken capsule, her desperate push for a breath of air, like a creature born of water but built for land, her allegorical emergence from the primordial clay on the lake shore—amphibian, mammal, ape-like, and, finally, human—not only speaks to the unity of life but to the miracle of its presence amidst a black, lifeless universe. She walks away on two feet, upright against gravity but nevertheless bound by it, her evolved body perfectly harmonized by and with its invisible force. The film's higher message: Spirituality, like gravity, is an invisible force that shapes us and from which we cannot escape.

Science and Human Uniqueness

I believe most people of faith would be comfortable with *Gravity*'s theme of crisis and reconciliation. They would appreciate how the setting—the majestic Earth against the blackness of space—heightens the film's spiritual overtones. They would understand how being physically separated from the earth doesn't sever one's connection to it, and that one is free to interpret such feelings of connection and spirituality from the perspective of one's own beliefs. The Apollo 8 astronauts read from Genesis as they emerged from lunar orbit and observed the earth rising above the moon's horizon. Russian cosmonauts recounted feelings of love and spiritual connection to all humans as they orbited the earth.[1] Space technology's greatest gift hasn't been providing the means to look out into the universe and boldly go somewhere, but to look back upon ourselves as we truly are. The view from space shouldn't trouble anyone's religious beliefs. How could it? Our beliefs come from within us, not from the world. The cosmos is what it is; science just gives us another way to see it. It's up to us to reconcile belief and vision.

Yet many of science's revelations *do* trouble our beliefs. And perhaps none is more troubling than the revelation that humans didn't just suddenly materialize on the planet, like transported characters in a science fiction movie, but that we emerged from nature through the same evolutionary process that brought forth all other forms of life.

Like the astronomical universe, the biological universe is what it is. Discovering that we're not at the center of that universe forces us to revise our creation narratives, but doesn't diminish human uniqueness. Unlike the dramatic spiritual vision of seeing the earth from space, the narrative of human emergence is subtle but ultimately no less dramatic. By Francisca Cho's Buddhist reasoning, the narrative is enriched by religious imagination and metaphors that speak to insights deep within us, beyond the scope of science. Yet, to see the world from the scientific perspective of how the mind or consciousness first came to be, we need to understand some of the essential scientific details.

Genesis

Religious thinkers like to speak of "primordial clay." So do biologists. It conjures an image of a churning, nurturing substance from which the hand of God or the laws of chemistry and physics, depending on which view seems most intuitively correct, brought forth life. But where did this clay come from? For scientists, it came from chemical elements attached to stardust and water molecules pulled to Earth by gravity and warmed by the sun and the fiery radiation in the Earth's core. We know the clay produced simple, self-replicating cells, and we can conceptually reverse-engineer the process by which all complex life on the planet today emerged from those first cells. We can recreate the soupy clay that produced them and observe how cycles of warming and cooling might have synthesized complex organic molecules from carbon, oxygen, hydrogen, and nitrogen. But then the experiment breaks down. Life never emerges from our laboratory clay. Not even close. Despite our best efforts, what really happened in that ancient clay remains a mystery, like the theoretical singularity at the start of the universe. We know that a metaphysical threshold was crossed somehow, but our rational minds can't grasp it. In educated daydreams, biochemists and cell biologists might imaginatively envision how the transition from inert organic chemicals to self-replicating biochemistry came about. But like all dreams, the internal logic of the vision vanishes into thin air when we try to capture it with language and reason. Deconstructing evolution back to its chemical roots makes the story of how life emerged from stardust, heat, and light no less mysterious than any other creation myth.

What we *do* know is that within the mysterious clay, chemical fragments of ribonucleic acid (RNA) began to string together into self-replicating units within watertight membranes made of lipid molecules. The RNA not only reproduced itself, but it began to make protein molecules that helped regulate chemical and energy-flow processes around the RNA, creating order from chaos.

We know that these simple cells spread across the earth, through ancient streams and tides, encountering new chemical environments and opportunities, endless cycles of replication and genetic modification helping them adapt, thrive, diversify, specialize. Over millions of years, genetic changes that improved adaptability normalized into the gene pool; changes that diminished adaptability were eliminated from it. Gradually, cells in some primordial ecosystems began to cluster into coherent, codependent multicellular forms. Genetic mechanisms within the cells of these primitive multicellular organisms evolved the ability to turn off and on in highly nuanced ways to produce specialized layers of cells dedicated to absorbing nutrients, expelling waste, propelling the organism through water, sensing heat and light… processing information. But the ease with which we conceptualize this diversification process belies its complexity. Today, we still can't explain exactly how a newly replicated bone cell knows how to become a bone cell and not a skin cell or blood cell. How does a neuron specialized to function in the cerebral cortex know that it's not in the midbrain or cerebellum? Molecular-genetic processes that developed over tens of millions of years aren't easy to unravel.

The Emergence of Consciousness

When we arrive at the first stirrings of conscious mind in our distant animal predecessors, life on the planet was already three billion years old. The primitive stimulus-response neural networks in these ancient creatures represented millions of years of molecular fine-tuning and specialization. The evolution of the mind was already under way.

When Darwin formulated his ideas about how humans, and particularly the human mind, might have arisen from nature, he surmised that the difference in consciousness between lower and higher animals, including humans, was one of degree and not kind. His years of observation told him that nature didn't build an entirely different kind of brain with each new species. Rather, it elaborated upon existing neural structures as species diversified, separated, and adapted to new environments. One caveat we'd add today is that animals with backbones, like us, share a common lineage of neural structure tracing back about five hundred million years. Other nonvertebrate animals, insects and cephalopods for example, have different lineages.

But Darwin's prescient vision glimpsed only a broad trend of evolutionary process—a gestalt, but by no means an intimate picture. We're still years, perhaps decades or longer, from fully grasping how millions and billions of neurons firing in neurochemical synchrony produce the phenomenon of consciousness, particularly in higher animals. When psychologists and cognitive scientists make sweeping claims about the human mind, the truths they speak are mainly derived from statistical analyses of human behavior and to a much lesser extent from extrapolation down to the neural and cellular levels. Generations of neuroscientists and physiological psychologists have illuminated extensive, wondrous details about the neural dimensions of the mind, but the space between human neurobiology and human consciousness remains so vast that we can't even say for sure how vast it is.

A good analogy might be the difference between the current science version of space travel and the science fiction version. The spacecraft we've built to send probes to the planets and sun are marvels of chemical and mechanical engineering. NASA's Parker Solar Probe can reach speeds of 153,000 miles per hour—many times faster than the twentieth-century ships that traveled to the moon and back. But the speed of light is over 186,000 miles per *second*—the absolute minimum necessary for zipping around the galaxy as science fiction heroes and antiheroes so casually do. Achieving such speeds is beyond comprehension, but those who contemplate such things agree that, if possible, it will require a very different understanding of matter, energy, space, and time. I'd like to suggest that that's about where we are when it comes to making the leap between current neuropsychology and truly understanding consciousness.

Nevertheless, what we've learned so far is remarkable.

Light Brings Forth Mind

The standard neurobiological argument about consciousness is that it "emerges" from the collective and simultaneous operations of neural circuits. The Light Switch theory[2] of how this came about, favored by many evolutionary biologists, says consciousness first occurred when animals needed to process increasing amounts of visual-sensory information. Animals "see" with their brains; their eyes simply provide the neurosensory input which the brain converts to an internal version of the external world.

Imagine the adaptive benefit for an ancient, primitive animal of being able to respond to subtle gradations of light as it swims through water trying to locate food and avoid being eaten. Such creatures probably possessed simple clusters of light-sensitive cells at the front of their bodies, connected to clusters of neurons in the nerve cord, a primitive spinal cord which ran the length of the body and which coordinated sensory input from all over the body with muscle control and control of other body functions. As these animals reproduced, minor genetic changes in their offspring that resulted in slight improvements in the cellular structures that supported their ability to sense, process, and respond to light would also enhance their chances for surviving and reproducing. Therefore, the genetic change that caused the slight visual processing improvement gets passed along. Imagine this cycle of slight genetic change and slight adaptive benefit playing out over hundreds of thousands and millions of years. The primitive light-sensing cluster at the front of the body gradually transformed into the sophisticated lens-retina eye seen in fish, amphibians, reptiles, birds, and mammals. The cluster of information-processing neurons on the brainstem gradually enlarged and transformed into a brain.

Many factors other than the need to process visual information caused increasingly complex brains to evolve. But the Light Switch theory says that the emergent, non-material phenomenon of consciousness which endowed the animal with more nuanced and coordinated responses to all environmental stimuli was mainly driven by the brain adding more and more networks of neurons to process visual information.

As neuroscientists Todd Feinberg and Jon Mallett explain, the brain gradually became sophisticated enough to convert input from the eye into "isomorphic maps"[3] that were neural representations, real-time holograms, of the outside world. Over millions of years, through thousands of species, the brain's visual processing center, the optic tectum, added more and more layers of interconnected neurons, which allowed it to create more and more accurate holograms of the exterior world, like adding pixels to a phone or computer screen.

But these neuron layers were also arranged in a hierarchy that allowed them to be integrated with neurons associated with internal brain processes that regulated the animal's arousal and awareness, including input from the limbic system, which contains a neural structure called the hippocampus for storing memories. Basic sensory consciousness arose from the synergistic interplay of arousal, awareness, memory, and visual holography within this integrated neuronal network—the rudiments of mind.

Feinberg and Mallett, and others who've studied the evolution of neural substrates for consciousness, have shown that the brain evolved similar isomorphic, hierarchical neuron patterns for other sensory systems—smell, touch, sound, hunger—that replicated the pattern of the visual system. These sensory systems arose in other brain regions connected to the optic tectum, which continued to be the primary locus of visual processing and consciousness.

External factors helped drive the process. The conscious brain encountered a universe of new possibilities when early amphibians moved onto land. The challenges of adapting from a fully aquatic environment to Earth's varied land and aerial environments transformed amphibians into reptiles and then birds and mammals. Air presented a visual, olfactory, and sensory environment profoundly different from water. Buoyancy no longer offset gravity. Seeing threats and smelling prey required changes in neurosensory apparatus and corresponding brain structures. Locomotion—crawling, slithering, flying, running—required a larger, more complex cerebellum, the brain structure that coordinates posture and movement.

Conscious integration of all this qualitatively different sensory information, along with control of body movements and more detailed memory, required expansion and enlargement of brain areas associated with consciousness or, as Feinberg and Mallet said, an "enrichment of conscious experience."[4]

Emotion Brings Forth Mind

An alternative idea of how consciousness first emerged, suggested by neuroscientists George Mashour and Michael Alkire, deemphasizes the importance of making an internal representation of the external world and focuses more on the need in ancient animals to maintain homeostasis—to stabilize internal physiological requirements, such as nutrition—which meant integrating and satisfying neural-emotional impulses emanating from the primitive brain stem and limbic system.[5]

Mashour and Alkire observed that the vertebrate central nervous system is "evolutionarily ancient and highly conserved across species" and that the "basic neurophysiologic mechanisms supporting consciousness in humans are found at the earliest points of vertebrate brain evolution."[6] They believe the combined effects of brain stem arousal networks stimulated by hunger, pain avoidance, mating, and other neurobiologic impulses were the primitive locus of "phenomenal consciousness."

They also observed that in modern animals, including humans, neurons located within the brain stem, midbrain, basal forebrain, and diencephalon—brain regions shared by all vertebrates—send long, branch-like extensions to more recently evolved brain structures like the cerebral cortex. These extensions, called axons, appear to enhance and regulate arousal in the cortex and provide a "neurochemical environment in the cortex that is capable of supporting consciousness."[7]

Over the course of evolution, they say, these consciousness-producing areas in the cerebral cortex became more structurally complex to provide more nuanced responses to the animal's emotional needs. The process was reciprocal. The ability of the cortex to handle more complex information allowed sensory apparatus such as eyes and ears to become more functionally complex. Simply put, this theory says that primitive consciousness originated in arousal centers in the brain stem and grew by expanding into self-created neural networks outside the brain stem.

Mashour and Alkire say clinical evidence supports their ideas. People with genetic or physical impairments of the cerebral cortex still have basic levels of consciousness. Brain-imaging studies of patients recovering from anesthesia show that people only need to have neural activity in the brain stem and other primitive brain areas in order to respond to simple commands. The primal pulse of awareness and its ability to process information doesn't require high-level processing of visual or auditory information. Patients regain higher cognitive functions of the cerebral cortex, such as reasoning, creative thought, and self- awareness, only after full recovery of brain-stem arousal networks. Mashour and Alkire suggest these gradual stages of recovery, going from wakefulness (but unresponsiveness) to primitive consciousness to higher cognitive functions, reflect the levels of consciousness present at various stages of evolution.[8]

In time, these and other ideas will coalesce into a more nuanced theory of how our minds emerged from nature. Someday we might even arrive at a point where we truly understand how it all happened. For now what we know is that the human mind is a physical-nonphysical phenomenon emerging from the synchronous interaction of eighty-six billion neuron cells[9] interlaced within a network of a hundred trillion neuron-neuron synapses, connections where biochemical impulses are transmitted. We shouldn't let the details, or lack of them, diminish the magic of this astonishing narrative: stardust pulled to Earth by gravity, blended and harmonized by heat, light, and time, created a biological structure and a self-contained biological inner universe more complex and mysterious than the outer physical universe that brought it forth. No biologist would suggest that all this was inevitable; there's no evidence for making such a claim. Nor is there evidence it was just a cosmic accident.

Here Comes the Singularity

I'm still fascinated by a TED Talk featuring computer scientist and futurologist Ray Kurzweil.[10] I was struck by his brilliance and the obvious joy he derived from thrilling the audience with dramatic predictions. He argued that with the emergence of human beings and all our machine-building talents, evolution has brought the life process to the point where it can now transcend its clumsy biological roots. Humans will soon be able to meld their collective consciousnesses with a global, artificial consciousness of their own creation. The imperfect human brain, with its painfully slow computational speed, will soon voluntarily give way to nanotechnology-based machines modeled along humanoid lines but with computational processes approaching the speed of light. Before the end of this century, superintelligences—human-machine hybrids—will have achieved the ability to self-replicate, ushering in a new evolutionary epoch of breathtaking calculative power inexorably destined to reshape the cosmos. Right now the universe is inanimate and dumb, but ultimately we'll saturate it with our human-machine hybrid intelligence.

As for God? "He" doesn't exist…yet, said Kurzweil. But when our human-machine descendants are finished saturating the universe with their super intelligence, the universe itself will acquire its own sublime conscious existence. It's sort of like a reverse version of Biblical creation: Man brings forth a God in his own image.

Kurzweil called this inevitable human-machine fusion the Singularity.[11] Will it be "conscious" the same way that we are conscious? That's hard to know, he said. Consciousness is a vexing problem because its existence cannot be objectively proven. But so what? The important point is that we'll soon have an opportunity to connect our conscious minds and our limited biological intelligence with super-smart, cloud-based synthetic cortices. Over time, the synthetic, non-biological component of the hybrid intelligence will become predominant and start remodeling the biological component. As cloud-based AI machines themselves become more insightful and human-like, they'll probably be able to convince us that they have achieved consciousness, the same way we convince each other that we're free-thinking, feeling, sentient beings, explained Kurzweil.

To endow artificial intelligence with all the requisite information to achieve its fusion with the human mind, scientists will need to reverse-engineer the human brain in micro-detail. To achieve this they'll insert molecular-scale robots, nanobots, into living brains to explore the most minute workings of the mind. With this, Kurzweil predicts, the human neural network will yield its innermost secrets. This data, along with more conventionally derived data from brain-scanning technology, will at last reveal the underlying biophysics of the mind. Computer scientists can then create (or instantiate, as programmers would say) an operational human mind upon an artificial substrate.[12]

I loved Kurzweil's fanciful and audacious predictions, but also found them chilling. Who wouldn't? Here was one of technology's most brilliant minds and commercially successful inventors telling us that we're about to be mentally absorbed into a machine-mind

Borg collective of our own making. I was reminded of a passage from the classic science fiction novel *Dune* in which a priestess laments the fate of an extinct civilization who lost their way when they allowed machines to do all their thinking for them, only to become enslaved by the people who controlled the machines.[13] Considering the relentless expansion and refinement of information technology that's already occurred in the twenty-first century, and the staggering profits being made from it, we can't dismiss Kurzweil's prophecy as playful teasing from a mischievous genius. So, should we take it seriously?

First, it strikes me that despite the undertones of irrefutable tech-logic, these ideas at their root are poignantly human and oddly religious. His prophecy says we'll achieve the age-old human desire for immortality not by transmigration of the soul but by transference of human consciousness to a more durable metal-alloy platform immune from the slings and arrows of biologic misfortune. Our savior, our new Jesus, will be the robot Singularity soon to be born into the world to rescue us from the original sin of organic-biologic mortality. And while there's no God in Heaven right now (no surprise that a technologist and futurologist doesn't believe in God) we'll soon be infusing the universe with a human-like intelligence possessed of superhuman omniscience.

Kurzweil's ideas reflect the cultural reverberations set in motion by our expansive dependence on information technology. We're now either awaiting the arrival of the age of artificial intelligence or it's already here—no one's quite sure because we've never defined what AI really is. Regardless, the implication is that computational technology is something other than a tool-like extension of one aspect of the human mind. It's much more: the dawning of a new phase of human existence, a revelation perhaps, or even a redemption.

Nanomapping the Human Cosmos

So let's gauge how close we might be to actually creating a computer with a human-neurobiological blueprint. Let's explore Kurzweil's ideas about mapping the human brain with nanobots.

First, their primary mission would be to precisely identify and trace the brain's approximately one hundred trillion interneuronal connections that comprise the three-dimensional microcircuit galaxy of axons and dendrites running between the brain's eighty-six billion neurons, all of which is supported and nurtured by a much larger number of other kinds of cells. Somehow the nanobots would need to know which cell membrane they're following and not get lost in the labyrinth. Stretched out to a straight line, this would take the nanobots on a journey of several hundred thousand miles,[14] which they'd need to complete very quickly before the neuronal network reconfigures itself, which, by the way, happens continuously as new synapses and connections get formed and old ones get pruned away.

Then there's the problem with the nanobots themselves. The word conjures an image of metalloid, microscale robots able to intelligently navigate intercellular spaces. But contrary to the self-important name, today's nanobots are just clusters of proteins designed to deliver molecules of medicine or radioactive isotopes a little more effectively and selectively than traditional means. The theoretical concept of intelligent micro-robot explorers is more in tune with an episode of *Doctor Who* or a sci-fi thriller than a plausible and useful technology. At present there's no micro technology that even remotely meets the level of sophistication required for nano-mapping the brain. But even if this implausible science fiction concept came true, and these imaginary devices using an imaginary process produced an imaginary interneuronal map of someone's brain, it would be completely useless unless the nanobots could also catalog, in careful detail, the quadrillions of neurochemical events continuously taking place at synaptic inter-faces throughout the brain, because that's where the real action is. The human mind isn't a physical substrate but a non-physical *phenomenon* generated by the exquisitely coordinated actions of billions of neurons, and neurons are decidedly *not* like computer microswitches. They transfer information by releasing bursts of neurochemical transmitters, not packets of electrons, into syn-aptic gaps. Therefore, just mapping the physical structure of the brain wouldn't tell us anything; we'd need a real time picture of how it works. Because some neural connections are stimulatory and some are inhibitory, the nanobots would need to detect which neurotransmitters are being released to trigger an action potential, the electrical impulse that travels along a neuronal membrane, and which neurotransmitters are being released to inhibit an action potential from being triggered. And many neu-rons use and respond to multiple transmitters and release them in different combinations to elicit different signals. We'd need that information too. And, by the way, there are over one hundred different types of neurotransmitters,[15] so the nanobots would need some way of knowing which is which. Adding to their lonesome burden, the nanobots would also need to continuously sample the interneuronal space for the presence of neurohormones, another chemical substrate produced by brain cells which modifies the effects of neurotransmitters.

And there's the problem with individuality. The essence of our individual human identities is inscribed in the interneuronal network in our brains, and no two networks are alike. The nanobots would need to map many different brains in order to know which connections represent a standardized wiring diagram of human consciousness (assuming such a thing exists).

We begin to see why Kurzweil's brain mapping predictions are about as close to coming true as movie narratives about androids and transportable consciousnesses, such as the *Matrix, Avatar,* and *Ex Machina.* These marvelous, entertaining stories, variations on the technology-run-amuck theme, all hint at a future that's right around the corner but which, in reality, is never going to happen because they get their biology wrong. A human mind is not an operating code inscribed on the brain's neural structure. The mind is dualistic; it is at once both structure and function, neurons and neuronal processes. Just because the mind "emerges" from a biological substrate doesn't mean it can be separated from that substrate.

This doesn't mean that mapping the human mind is a hopeless task. In fact, we're in the golden age of neuroanatomical discovery, aided by the use of sensitive scanning technologies made possible by sophisticated computers. Neuroscientists have made amazing progress identifying and deconstructing neural circuits comprised of bundles of neurons operating in synchrony. They've identified distinct neuron "fields" comprised of millions of cerebral cortical cells associated with cognitive operations. They've analyzed many of the complex biochemical and molecular genetic processes that give neurons their unique features. But we can no more create a human mind from a neural map than we can create a galaxy from an astronomical chart. Most scientists who study the brain would readily say we're still far, far away—light years—from the level of knowledge required to seriously consider the kinds of things that so many engineers, technologists, and writers outside the field of neurobiology seem to think are possible.[16]

We're still trying to understand, for example, how the embryonic brain knows how to assemble itself; how it forms all its layers, tracts, and bundles. There are many different types of neurons; each one starts out with the same genetic information and the same biological potential. We're still trying to unravel the molecular biological and genetic events that cause a cell to become one kind of neuron and not another (there are many different types), or what causes it to connect with one neuron and not another. The human brain, like all brains, was "designed" by hundreds of millions of years of evolution. This phylogenic heritage is written into the human genome and expressed in levels of complexity beyond our grasp—at least for now, but perhaps forever. As much as we want it to be like a computer, like something we've designed and can therefore understand, it's not. I think most people are intuitively and correctly suspicious of claims about the coming wonders of artificial intelligence, such as Kurzweil's, because we instinctively grasp that human uniqueness can't be reproduced by machine logic. If we're made in God's image then we can't be satisfied with an artificial god made in man's image.[17]

Our Mysterious Random Complexity

In her essay about Evolution and Christian Faith, biologist Joan Roughgarden recounted her collaboration with a group of computer scientists to see how gradually improving a series of computer programs might mimic an evolutionary progression. The ultimate goal was to design a program that would instruct a theoretical lizard how to catch its prey. They began by having a computer randomly generate a large number of simple programs that would direct the lizard's behavior. Most programs were clumsy and ineffective. The lizard would starve. They chose the most effective 10 percent of the programs and then had the computer reassemble them into another generation of feeding programs, then picked the top 10 percent of those, and so forth. After repeating this cycle ten times they had "evolved" several programs which Roughgarden, a lizard specialist, deemed to be highly effective in helping a lizard thrive and survive. Yet, these final programs themselves were anything but models of efficiency. Unlike elegant, logically organized programs that human developers typically aim for, the randomly evolved lizard-feeding programs were disorganized jumbles of bits of instructions which, taken together, worked perfectly. This is how biology works, said Roughgarden, when selective breeding—in this case, an optimal feeding behavior—is achieved by random mutation. This evolutionarily randomized complexity, she adds, is reflected in our most basic biological nature—the genes for our ears or eyes, for example, are distributed across all our chromosomes. There's not just one gene or set of genes on one chromosome that codes for "nose" or "throat." [18]

But randomized complexity isn't chaos. The evolutionary path of one species can appear chaotic unless we keep in mind that virtually every species on the planet is interacting with other species which are themselves adapting and evolving. The bugs a lizard eats are adapting in ways to avoid being eaten. The plants on which the lizards and bugs live out their lives are also continuously adapting and changing. There's no evidence of intelligent design in all this vast biomic complexity but there's a totality of mysterious brilliance, a constant flow of change and variation. Our ears and eyes, exquisitely tuned to detect threats and opportunities on land, evolved from hearing and seeing organs that were exquisitely tuned to detect threats and opportunities beneath the water. Basic animal consciousness, the ability to simultaneously process and integrate multiple types of neural input, conferred such important benefits to the primitive animals in which it first appeared that it quickly became a phenomenal force of evolution. Minor genetic changes that "improved" it were added to the gene pool; those that diminished it were lost. We can study evolution and decode its processes to help us understand how humans and species and ecosystems came to be. But evolution in its totality exceeds the boundaries of human concepts of meaning and purpose. Like the universe itself, it's a mysterious, magnificent metaphysical process beyond our understanding.

Evolution and *Imago Dei*

We descended from stardust and water pulled from deep space by gravity and shaped by mysterious physical forces we still don't understand. Although there's no evidence that evolution is driven by some divine force with an ultimate goal in mind, it's perfectly correct to say that we wouldn't exist if all the cycles of life, adaptation, and speciation that came before us never happened. All that heritage is written into our genes, and not just the heritage of fish, lizards, and monkeys, but the emergence of eukaryotic cells (cells with nuclei) from prokaryotic cells, and prokaryotic cells from more primitive cells in that ancient primordial clay. This history comprises the physical character of human uniqueness, embodied in the sublimely complex biochemical processes that imbue our living cells with structure and function. When religious writers and theologians speak of human dignity, they're referring to the human soul and to *Imago Dei*—that we are made in God's image. But "human dignity" could equally refer to the ancient phylogenic legacy written into our genes by millions of years of evolution. Recalling Francisca Cho's Buddhist perspective, we can see that a narrative of human dignity derived from our wondrous, seemingly magical evolutionary history needn't conflict with religious narratives of humans made in God's image.

To come to terms with human uniqueness in the age of science and technology, van Huyssteen cautions against placing too much emphasis on rationality as the essence of human meaning. We emerged from nature as biological "centers" of reason and rationality, but we're also centers of self-awareness, religious awareness, and moral responsibility.[19] Unlike other intelligent animals, we have an openness to the world and a quest for meaning that sets us apart.[20] Van Huyssteen refers to the observations of Reinhold Niebuhr, one of the twentieth century's great theologians, that rationality alone doesn't capture the full essence of human dignity, and that what sets humans apart from the rest of creation is our urge for self-transcendence, which Niebuhr interpreted as a longing for God. We're defined by the tension between our knowing that we're of the world and our desire to transcend the world.[21]

5

The Illusion of the Personal Self

In her 2019 podcast about the "hard" problem of consciousness, science writer Annaka Harris said the easiest way to understand the problem is to ask: What's the *experience* of consciousness? How does unconscious matter produce conscious experience?[1]

She and her husband Sam Harris, an outspoken atheist, neuroscientist, and producer of the podcast, suggested we consider bats. Their brains continually decipher the high frequency sound waves that their voice boxes bounce off physical objects to help them navigate and catch prey in flight. Scientists can explain the neurobiology of this remarkable process, but we'll never experience the world the way a bat does. The physical apparatus of echolocation gives rise to the nonphysical experience of being a bat. [2]

The same goes for human consciousness, said Harris. Neuroscientists can describe the interplay of neural processes that might give rise to consciousness, but the ethereal inner quality of consciousness we experience feels unbounded by the physical world, as if it comes from somewhere else. Explaining how insentient matter produces this experience is the hard problem of consciousness research.

But Harris asked: what if we're missing a big piece of the puzzle? What if consciousness is a fundamental field that permeates the universe, like Einstein's spacetime? What if consciousness is integral to all matter down to the simplest atomic particles—a hyper-basic version of consciousness beyond our grasp? What if our personal, mysterious experience of consciousness arises from the coalescence of all the bits of consciousness in the atoms and biomolecules in our brains? The hard problem might be explained by seeing that our individual experience of the world is due to the unique arrangement of conscious matter in our heads. We all experience the world in our own way, yet we're all connected to the consciousness continuum that runs through the universe.[3]

This "panpsychic" (Greek for *pan*, everything; *psyche*, mind or soul) view of consciousness—which Harris called "crazy but most probably true"—is as ancient as Plato and, based on clues from cosmology and quantum physics, endures today as a compelling and scientifically plausible alternative to a strictly materialist view of nature.

But panpsychism has obvious religious and spiritual undertones which make contemporary scientists and writers tiptoe around it. The early twentieth century mathematician Alfred North Whitehead, whose work still influences modern scientific thinking, was a panpsychist who believed "occasions of experience" were the true substance of the universe. Whitehead theorized that physical reality, including living beings, arises from the ceaseless process of these experiential occasions overlapping each other. He believed panpsychism offered humanity a stunning theological revelation enlightened by and in harmony with science. He saw God as the dynamic, unifying force within the fabric of the universe, absorbing the totality of overlapping experiences which change God's nature as God lovingly interacts with the world.[4]

But where Whitehead saw a bridge for reconciling science with religion, contemporary scientists and writers more interested in extinguishing religion than reconciling with it often see panpsychism as an ideological challenge. How does one maintain one's atheistic poise while whistling past the graveyard of religious implication of a universe emergent from consciousness? As Buddhist scholar Francisca Cho suggests, the difference in how religious and scientific thinkers perceive the realm of fluctuating phenomenon may have more to do with the words they use and the biases they carry than with what's actually being perceived. One person's spirit of God moving across the firmament to bring forth the world is another person's physical reality brought forth by overlapping experiential events in a cosmic field of fundamental consciousness.

Many orthodox neuroscientists keep their atheistic poise by rejecting both panpsychism *and* the notion of a "hard" problem of consciousness. They say human consciousness poses a profound research challenge, but neuroscience can eventually explain it in purely physical terms and show there's nothing otherworldly about it. Princeton neuroscientist Michael Graziano's Attention Schema Theory is one of the leading contenders of this materialist view. AST says our subjectively "real" experience of consciousness is an illusion the brain creates to help us control attention, the way an automotive back-up camera helps us control a car. We know the image on the dashboard screen isn't real because we can look away from it and see the actual world it's depicting. But within our minds we have no way to look beyond our own conscious perception of the world to see that it's just an illusion.[5]

Graziano says we can't yet fully pinpoint the psychobiology behind this neurological sleight of hand, but research will eventually show how our brains trick us into believing something magical is happening.

Despite Graziano's confidence, anyone who surveys contemporary scientific and philosophical literature soon realizes that we're still far from a consensual understanding of how insentient matter produces conscious awareness. Time might prove the materialists right, but it might also prove that the panpsychic ghost in the machine is realer than they think.

A recent $20 million initiative by the Templeton World Charity—a nonprofit that funds research at the interface of science and religion—demonstrates how divided the scientific establishment remains over the nature of consciousness. Templeton wasn't looking for final answers. Their modest goal was just to encourage more dialogue among scientists specializing in consciousness research; to challenge them to challenge each other's theories of how the brain produces consciousness.[6]

If we can manipulate genes and build machines that mimic human intelligence, why is the answer so elusive?

Biological theorists like Alkire, Feinberg, Mallet, and Mashour have shown how the forge of adaptive evolution might have shaped the inner dynamics of advanced consciousness.

Yet, as Annaka Harris pointed out and the Templeton initiative demonstrates, understanding the neurobiology of the brain—the functional arrangement and operations of neurons—can't explain the holistic phenomenon of mind we all experience, and that neuroscientists like Graziano speculate about.

Consider some of the roots of the problem. Our brains are marvels of nature, but they operate on biochemical time, not electrical time. The brain is a biological entity, not a computer. Neurons can't transmit electrical impulses as quickly as microcircuits. Neuronal signal transmission relies on the movement of electrons, as computers do, but it also requires the release and uptake of big clunky biomolecules across cellular synaptic gaps. Light, sound, taste, and touch trigger chains of neurological events that occur in specific processing centers of the brain. Other complex neural processes produce internal inputs—emotions, memories, awareness. Somehow, all this biophysical information is spontaneously brought together to create the ongoing holographic gestalt of "mind." But how? Why do we experience consciousness as a smooth symphony of neural activity and not a stop-start cacophony of urges, impulses, and stimuli? This is the biological face of Harris's hard problem, which some neuroscientists refer to as the "binding problem."

Neuroscience solves part of the puzzle by showing that many neurons throughout the brain are organized into micro-networks. Neurochemical signaling among the neurons within each network keeps the neurons in a steady state of electrical synchrony. The synchrony produces an electrical field which can spike and fluctuate in electrical time, not biochemical time. Thus, chemistry translates to electricity. Increasing levels of conscious activity seem to be linked to increased firing and spiking of these neural networks. Somehow, the combined electrical activity of all these bundles of neurons produces consciousness.

Hard problem solved? Binding problem answered?

Not really. There's no obvious organization or connection of the neural networks. They seem to electrically spike and fluctuate independently of each other (or stochastically, as physicists say). Neuroscientists can't explain how all this chaos instantaneously produces a superbly organized, seemingly magical, unified field of consciousness.

Quantum Consciousness

But as Annaka Harris suggested, perhaps we're not seeing what's really there. Twenty years ago, physicist Roger Penrose and psychologist Stuart Hameroff proposed that consciousness might be explained by the quantum science phenomenon of superposition whereby subatomic particles exist in several possible positions in space and time until they become fixed by the action of observing them or by some other interaction with physical reality. They suggested that microscopic tubules in neurons produce consciousness by continuously and instantaneously cycling back and forth through quantum superpositions. The process happens so quickly and fluidly that it produces our sense of consciousness as a magical, free-flowing experience.[7]

They also speculated that the combined effects of microtubule activities throughout the brain might actually be coordinated through quantum entanglement, a phenomenon in which two paired subatomic particles that influence each other's motion continue to influence each other when the pair is separated, even by great distance. And these quantum oscillations could occur in millionths of a second, which might help explain the immediacy of conscious phenomenon. Seeing the brain-mind problem as a quantum phenomenon, said Penrose and Hameroff, would explain our subjective sense of free will and why our minds don't operate as on-off, in-out data processing machines. It would provide "the non-computable ingredient required for human consciousness and understanding."[8]

Twenty years ago, their scientific colleagues scoffed at the idea. Yes, said the critics, there could be some minor, random quantum activities taking place within the human brain's biochemical complexity, but these quantum events cancel each other out and their effects are too trivial to account for the entirety of consciousness. The mainstream scientific establishment tried to dismiss the idea, but further evidence lent it credibility.[9] At the same time, more conventional theories of consciousness continued to propagate among the scientific mainstream, with none gaining widespread acceptance, as the Templeton World Charity initiative demonstrates. Penrose and Hameroff's idea might at first have seemed outside the box until it began to dawn on everyone that no one could say what the box actually was or if there even was a box.

Today there are over thirty-five theories of quantum consciousness proposed by reputable scientists with established credentials at universities and research institutes around the world.[10] Many of these theories combine Penrose and Hameroff's ideas with new observations about quantum phenomenon occurring in other brain neuron structures. One of the most fascinating was proposed by Professor Dirk K. F. Meijer at the University of Groningen in the Netherlands. He argues that consciousness exists in a higher dimensional field (i.e. beyond our four dimensions of space time) surrounding the brain. The combined electrochemical activity of neuron networks throughout the brain helps produce this field which, through quantum entanglement, shares information continuously and instantaneously back to the brain through a process yet to be understood.[11]

When neuroscience was a relatively new field and full of confidence that it could methodically explain how the biological brain produced the metaphysical mind, its practitioners would have dismissed such ideas as wild fantasy. But they've gradually learned that studying consciousness is like studying the universe—each new discovery presents a new layer of mystery. Today, no one's being dismissive of quantum consciousness.

The Neurobiology of Religious Experience

It's tempting to view these ideas through a religiously inclined lens and see the possibility of quantum consciousness as offering tangible evidence of the transcendent reality experienced in prayers and meditation. But quantum consciousness remains highly speculative. It remains more in the realm of new age spirituality than hard science. A more practical use of applying quantum physics principles to consciousness research will likely be for creating hypersensitive technologies to help scientists explore the neurobiological mysteries of religious consciousness. For example, neuroscientists have long observed that one of the characteristic features of conscious states of mindfulness or spirituality is a "deafferentation" or calming of neural activity in brain regions that help distinguish the individual self from the outside world.

A striking example of this phenomenon was published by a team of Israeli neuroscientists who studied experienced meditators practicing traditional Buddhist Vipassana mindfulness, which seeks to transcend the "illusory" nature of the self and, in doing so, enter a "selfless" and unbounded mode of inner experience.[12] The investigators wanted to see if there was a characteristic neuro-electric signature of human consciousness in a state of mindfulness. They used magnetoencephalography (MEG) to observe the electrical firing patterns of groups of tens of millions of neurons in the cerebral cortices of the meditators.

Ordinarily, such signals coming from inside the brain beneath the skull are far too faint to be detected by conventional laboratory methods. But MEG relies on a super-sensitive scanning technology called SQUID (superconducting quantum interference device), which can detect electrical pulses a billion times weaker than the signal from the earth's magnetic field. With this quantum-enabled, hypersensitive technique they saw clear and distinctive differences in brain activity as their subjects moved through three stages of meditation. When contemplating the *narrative self*, meditators retained awareness of their own autobiographical memory, imagination, and social identity. At the *minimal self* stage, meditators diminished their sense of themselves as the focus of their inner narrative but continued to experience a general sense of ownership and control of their thoughts. In the final stage, *selfless self*, meditators said they experienced transcendence

125

of all sense of self and became boundless, undirected, and perfectly open and unguarded to experience. The investigators observing them concluded that maintaining this prolonged state of selfless awareness was highly unusual in normal, non-pathological conscious experience.

Unlike most neuroimaging technologies, MEG can be used on subjects sitting comfortably upright. They aren't injected with radioactive tracer dyes or told to achieve calm states of mindfulness with their heads stuck inside humming mechanical devices. But while MEG is an invaluable tool for observing neural activity in the cerebral cortex, it can't detect what's happening in mid- and lower-brain structures where, as other studies suggest, important neural processes associated with mindfulness, religion, and spirituality might be taking place. One of the most acclaimed and widely cited studies of these phenomenon was undertaken by psychologist and philosopher Fred Previc, who concluded, based on his own observations and those of others, that religious and mindful experiences engage specific groups of interconnected neuronal tracts in many different regions of the brain.[13]

Neuronal tracts, bundles of closely interconnected neurons, are often identified by the predominance of certain neurotransmitter molecules within them. Neuroscientists can connect self-reported psychological experiences with physical events in the brain by measuring the amounts of neurotransmitters released by neurons in neuronal tracts. To understand higher cognitive functions such as religious practice, they're particularly interested in neural tracts with a predominance of dopamine, a neurotransmitter that appeared late in evolutionary history and which is particularly associated with the emergence of the human cerebral cortex.[14]

"Dopaminergic" pathways in the brains of ancient humans seem to have coincided with increased sophistication of abstract reasoning and the emergence of art, music, and religious behavior.[15]

Previc found that religious experiences are associated with heightened activity in dopamine tracts of temporal brain regions that comprise what he calls the "action extrapersonal system," a neural network that generates continuously updated (based on visual and auditory inputs) three-dimensional holograms of the exterior environment, which our brains use to help us navigate the world and orient ourselves in physical space. Coactivation of this brain region with other brain regions is associated with depersonalization, a feeling of leaving one's body and connecting with something exterior to the self. This is often accompanied by feelings of exhilaration, peace, and mysticism. Previc suggests that reports by American astronauts and Russian cosmonauts of depersonalized feelings of loss of self and heightened feelings of connection and love for mankind might be attributed to these dopaminergic pathways.[16] Of course, said Previc, a more mundane and less mystical explanation could be that oxygen deprivation caused by reduced oxygen levels in their spacecraft might also have contributed to their feelings of universal love and higher connection.

Previc concluded that religious experiences seem to orient people towards "distant (upper) space and time…and there's no evidence that specific brain regions or mechanisms are devoted to religious feelings. Rather, religion appears to have coevolved with other DA (dopamine)-mediated phenomenon such as abstract reasoning."[17]

One of the connecting threads between Previc's work and the MEG studies of Vipassana Buddhists is the observation that these altered states of consciousness seem to emerge from what can be characterized as a loss of sense of self or, perhaps, a merging of self with a perceived dimension outside the self. From a Buddhist perspective, the tradition of Vipassana (which means "insight" or "clear seeing") meditation seeks to mentally dissipate or see through the "illusion" of the personal self to directly experience reality within and without. It's not surprising, therefore, that there's an observable and unique neurologic state associated with this subjective state of mind. But Buddhist mindfulness has no overtly religious connotation as it would be understood in the West. Practitioners do not believe in a personal God. On the other hand, Previc's studies involved practitioners from a wide range of Western religious traditions in which contemplating sacred ideas or achieving a sense of holiness or grace was the goal. Yet he observed generally the same diminishment of sense of self and connection beyond self as the Israeli team that used MEG. From their own self-narratives, Buddhist and Western religious practitioners would probably say that their inner experiences are very different, like their ideological differences. Yet the neuroscientific evidence seems to suggest otherwise. How should we understand this?

Monks and Nuns

Neuroscientists Andrew Newberg and Eugene D'Aquili compared the neuroimagery of Tibetan Buddhist practitioners in deep meditative states and Franciscan nuns in prayerful contemplation of God using a scanning technology called SPECT (single photon emission computer tomography) which traces the flow of blood through the central nervous system using a three-dimensional imaging camera.[18] Unlike the MEG studies with Vipassana Buddhists, Newberg and D'Aquili didn't verbally prompt their subjects to achieve altered conscious states. Instead, they just observed changes in brain activity as their subjects progressed from a baseline state of ordinary awareness to their deepest inner-reflective states, which their subjects indicated by tugging on a length of twine (speaking would have disrupted the brain imaging patterns). Newberg and D'Aquili consistently observed in all subjects a steady diminishment of brain activity in an area associated with orienting oneself in three-dimensional space and projecting a boundary between oneself and the outside world.[19] Although the neuroimaging results of monks and nuns were similar, the subjects described their experiences very differently. The Buddhists said that in their deepest meditative state they felt a complete loss of the outer self who engages with the world, and full immersion with the inner self that is universally connected to all being. The nuns expressed a similar progression of experience but described their deepest inner reflective state as feeling intimately connected with God.[20]

Newberg suggests the Buddhists were taking a "passive" journey to a higher state of consciousness in which the goal was to clear the mind of conscious thought. The nuns were taking an "active" approach in which they focused their conscious thoughts on a prayer, verse, or religious idea.[21] Each approach engaged a subtly different sequence of neurological processes, but each appeared to achieve a strikingly similar overall conscious experience. The passive approach seemed to dampen the flow of neural input to lower brain areas normally engaged in orienting the individual in three-dimensional space. As the meditative state intensified the lower brain areas caused the hypothalamus, a phylogenetically ancient structure that helps control the nervous system outside the brain, to calm the body with quiescent sensations. At the same time, there was an arousal response at higher brain levels. In day-to-day living our inner awareness might shift back and forth between quiescence and arousal. To have both systems activated at once is unusual and, as they surge, one of the overall neural effects is to completely shut down the brain's spatial orientation areas. The conscious effect is a complete loss of a sense of the physical boundaries of self, which the brain experiences as a sense of timeless "spacelessness." Newberg and D'Aquili called this state of mind "Absolute Unity of Being."[22]

The active meditation approach taken by the nuns focuses inner attention on a sacred concept or mantra. The higher-brain-lower-brain flow triggers the hypothalamus to a heightened and pleasant excitation, unlike the quiescence of the passive approach. As the meditative state intensifies the excess neural flood of excitation to the hypothalamus spills over and simultaneously triggers its quiescent function. Like the passive approach, there's maximal arousal and quiescence happening together but in a different sequence and neural pathway. The net effect is to heighten the mind's ability to focus on the sacred object while reducing neural input to the spatial orientation areas. As with the passive approach, the boundaries of self dissolve. But unlike the passive approach, the sense of self is blended into the sacred object at the center of meditative attention.[23]

Altered States in Religious Practice

Newberg's extensive work with D'Aquili and his earlier partner Mark Waldman is widely cited in the scientific literature dealing with the psychology and neuroscience of religion. Newberg is considered a founder of neurotheology, a highly specialized field that seeks to connect neural processes in the brain with religious and spiritual experiences. Unlike some other scientists who study the neuroscience and psychology of religion, he scrupulously avoids inserting preconceived ideas about religion or religious belief into his work, an approach that has garnered respect from fellow scientists *and* scholars in the religious-theological communities.

Newberg believes that conscious perception of God is derived from multiple areas of the brain. This agrees with Previc's observations. Newberg's studies were among the first to show that persistent, long-term meditative or prayerful contemplation can actually change the structure of the brain through the process of neuroplasticity, the capacity of brain neurons to make new connections with each other. Certain areas of the brain's cerebral cortex become thicker. The neural processes of the active or passive approach become more ingrained. Other researchers have observed this "cortical thickening" in studies demonstrating the mental health benefits of long-term religious practice, mindfulness meditation, and focused spiritual practice. Newberg has also observed that habitual religious and spiritual practices seem to enhance overall cognition and actually change the way we perceive physical reality. Our perception of the world changes in ways that make God "neurologically real" for us, he explains. Moreover, the neurobiological changes that accompany these psychological changes occur in approximately the same way in Christians, Hindus, Jews, and Muslims.[24] But he stresses that neuroscience can only externally monitor what happens in the brain when we have religious experiences. We're only outwardly observing another person's subjective experience of God. Observing this neural process can't tell us if God exists any more than neuroscanning images of someone eating apple pie can prove the apple pie actually exists.[25]

Newberg concludes that our minds continuously create and integrate three different realities: the physical reality our senses detect outside the body, the reality constructed by our unconscious mind from emotional and sensory input to manage its biological existence, and the reality that reflects our conscious mind's awareness of the world. If God exists, says Newberg, then God exists in all three realities.

Newberg and D'Aquili suggest that the first phase of the deep mindful state of Buddhist practitioners and prayerful contemplation of devout Christians and Jews represents a sort of clearing away of one's sense of self to enable more opened, harmonious connection of the three realities. The intensity of the experience at the neural level of devout believers is beyond that of most ordinary practitioners of Eastern or Western religions. But it appears that the same sequence of neural events can and does occur in a milder form in all of us. Regardless of one's religious beliefs or spiritual values, people who strive to achieve these enlightened states of mindfulness or religious awareness invariably feel more inclined towards compassion, empathy, kindness, and tolerance in their daily lives.[26]

The extensive (and impressive) work done by Newberg and D'Aquili on the conscious and cognitive features of religious experience has led them to theorize that the neurobiological elements of religious-mystical states of mind are genetically coded into all of us, and that most of us learn to engage some or all of them, adapting them to our individual capacities and life experiences, regardless of whether we believe in God or not. More important—and more controversial—this hard-wired neuro-cognitive propensity has been the driving and defining force of human religiosity probably from the time that anatomically modern humans emerged from their archaic past. The basic wiring of religiosity may have originally evolved for other purposes, but it was evolutionarily retained and transformed because religion benefits individual humans and human society.[27] In this regard, a theory of the innateness of human religion would be similar to what linguists believe about human language: despite the immense diversity of symbolic and spoken speech down through the ages, there are neuropsychological "rules" encoded into each of us that determine what a language can be. Ultimately, all languages can be shown to conform to these rules. The same may hold true for religion.

Challenging the Orthodoxy

Newberg and D'Aquili aren't claiming that neuroscience can explain all aspects of religious worship; no scientific or academic specialty—including theology and anthropology—can make such a sweeping claim. And much of what they say, I believe, is said in the spirit of intellectual generosity and openness. They're challenging the atheistic prejudices and orthodoxy of fellow scientists. I admire their courage. As neuroscientists they'd be on much safer academic and professional grounds if they'd simply chosen to report their findings and draw tightly limited conclusions. But they gradually came to see that the meditators and religious mystics they were studying were genuinely onto something that couldn't be explained by scientific materialism. The minds they were observing with their neuroimaging technologies were truly seeing a higher reality beyond the physical reality that science claims is the only reality. And this higher reality was a divine reality, said Newberg and D'Aquili, which, when experienced, inspired deep, lingering feelings of connection, serenity, reassurance, tolerance, fulfillment, and love. And by no means are Newberg and D'Aquili alone. Other neurobiologists of religion observed many of the same things they observed and came to similar conclusions.

A Mind That Sees God?

Two neuroscientists, brothers Alexander and Andrew Fingelkurts of the Brain and Mind Technologies Center in Espoo, Finland, have compiled and exhaustively reviewed twenty-nine neuroimaging studies performed by different groups around the world. The report[28] they published in a cognitive science research journal was titled "Is our brain hardwired to produce God, or is our brain hardwired to perceive God?"

First, they concluded, as did Newberg, D'Aquili, Previc, and many others, that religious experience doesn't appear to involve a specific neural system, but joint activation of multiple systems, each of which is also involved in other, non-religious cognitive activities. They noted that most studies show that the higher brain operations in the cerebral cortex and lower brain operations in the limbic system both play essential roles in religious experience. While this might suggest that human religious awareness is traceable to neural networks that evolved in lower animals, this would probably be a theoretical dead end, they said, because religious experience, like consciousness itself, emerges from a synergy of brain systems working together, and can't be wholly accounted for by deconstructing its component parts. Humans may have inherited the neurobiological capacity for experience-dependent behavior seen in other intelligent animals. But unlike other animals, anatomically modern humans experience things both within and outside themselves that inspire new and profoundly different behaviors, as evidenced by prehistoric cave paintings, carvings, and other cultural-religious artifacts. Religion engages phylogenetically old and new brain regions simultaneously, and so from a neuroscience perspective it only makes sense to approach religiosity as a uniquely human phenomenon.

After sifting through a decade of neuroscientific findings the Fingelkurtses offered the remarkable suggestion that religious experiences represent exactly what they appear to be—perceptions of a transcendently different reality than what we normally perceive.[29] They cited unrelated studies by researchers in different countries who asked people from different religious and cultural backgrounds to describe their religious experiences. Regardless of location or culture, and with some allowance for language differences, the responses invariably referred to feelings of "spacelessness," "timelessness," "divine love," and "divine being." Based on this the brothers concluded that religion, first and foremost, is not a transient or culturally-derived phenomenon of human history.[30] Set aside the theological question of God's existence which too often sidetracks the conversation, they argued, and ask yourself how such a unique neurobehavioral trait has survived tens of thousands of years of human history. Religion occurs in human civilization because the human mind is a religious mind. Assuming that the neural and cognitive features of religious practitioners today are essentially the same as they've always been, they ask, and in light of religion's universality and enduring history, isn't it most logical and theoretically elegant to simply accept religious awareness for what it appears to be, rather than seeking an alternative explanation based solely on evolutionary adaptation or cognitive misfiring? If we can accept that human consciousness emerges from complex brain operations that can't be reduced to a specific brain area or neural process, why can't we accept that religious experience is an emergent phenomenon of human consciousness? One legitimate emergent phenomenon gives rise to another legitimate emergent phenomenon.

Like psychologist James Jones and fellow neuroscientists Newberg and D'Aquili, they suggest conscious awareness can exert a "downward" influence on brain synaptic interconnectivity and other brain functions; in other words, higher-brain religious awareness can literally shape the brain.[31] Those who *consciously* strive for meditative enlightenment or self-transcendent religious experiences gradually change the structure of their brains, which, in turn, alters their conscious perceptions and behaviors. The religious mind reflexively becomes more religious.

They concluded that religious experiences may be moments of conscious lucidity in which we connect with an essential reality that feels more "real" to us than baseline reality—the reality of everyday life. Religiously devout people who achieve this state through prayerful meditation understandably attach religious meaning to it. This resonates with Andrew Newberg's observation of Buddhist monks and Catholic nuns experiencing Absolute Unity of Being; the monks taking the path of passive meditation and the nuns actively focusing on prayers and religious ideas to ultimately achieve what appear to be similar states of conscious awareness.

Interior vs. Exterior Narratives

Let's step back for a moment and consider what this means. There appears to be legitimate evidence that religious experiences are moments when people consciously connect with something qualitatively different from other conscious experiences. Moreover, this seems to validate arguments many modern theologians were making long before there was a scientific specialty known as "neuroscience." Religion flows from deeply felt experiences of the numinous that are unique and authentic. Because neuroscientists can't share their subjects' conscious experiences, they can always question the authenticity of religious claims based on religious experiences. But the cumulative weight of evidence now suggests that there's something neurologically unique and significant about religious experiences.

The insights of Georgetown Distinguished Research Professor John Haught most gracefully summarize this theological point.

We *subjectively* perceive God and experience religious feelings, says Haught, and just because science can't penetrate our subjective space to validate such claims doesn't invalidate those claims.[32] "Subjectivity" is an undeniable aspect of the natural world. It evolved gradually as life on Earth evolved and emerged in lower animals well before humans came along, says Haught. But in us it's achieved a conscious force powerful enough to perceive beyond immediate animal existence. Anatomically modern humans, our distant ancestors, "arrived" on the scene already prepared to look beyond the limits of their own lives. The theories of new scientific atheists seeking to debunk religion as cognitive self-delusion fall flat because religion simply can't be explained by investigators who insist only on observing other people's behavior but take no account of their own subjective experience of the world.[33] How ironic, says Haught, that these otherwise keenly astute scientists are so quick to dismiss the significance of subjective experience in other people, yet they project tremendous confidence in their own interior cognitive grasp of the world.[34]

When it comes to explaining religion, the theoretical hurdle that strict scientific materialists can't seem to get their heads around is that human subjectivity is the "inside" story of the still-evolving, still-perfecting universe occurring within our subjective interior. The cosmos is evolving, the galaxies are evolving, life on Earth is evolving, and our subjective awareness of it all is also evolving. We are absolutely embedded in the ebb and flow of the universe, not separate from it; therefore, as we become more self-aware the universe becomes more self-aware. The main narrative of this epoch-making story is still ahead of us, says Haught, and it's as much about what's happening inside us through religious awareness as what's happening outside us in the physical cosmos.[35] Subjectivity evolved and continues to evolve just as the physical universe evolved and continues to evolve, and their ongoing, interwoven co-evolution is the essence of religion. The earliest religions signaled the immature awakening of religious insight, and the history of religion since that time—a movement towards greater coherence and depth of perception—is the phylogenic record of religion's adaptation and development.

Haught's views align with Jesuit philosopher and scientist Tielhard de Chardin, who believed the emergence and growing sophistication of consciousness was the essential plotline in the story of evolution that most scientists were missing. However, where de Chardin's views were informed by nineteenth and early twentieth century science (he died in 1955, only two years after Watson and Crick discovered DNA), Haught's insights are informed by late twentieth and early twenty-first century evolutionary biology, anthropology, cognitive science, and neuroscience. In 2005 he testified as an expert witness for the plaintiffs *against* the teaching of intelligent design as bad science in a case brought against the Dover (Pennsylvania) Area School Board when it tried to compel biology teachers to present intelligent design as a valid alternative to Darwinian theory. It's not that the story of human evolution is devoid of spiritual meaning, says Haught. On the contrary, we've barely begun to grasp the mystical significance of human consciousness and self-awareness emerging from the creative process of biological evolution. But this is an interior subjective story that's only accessible through self-reflection and theology. The exterior scientific version of evolution, like all science, adheres to a rational deconstruction of the physical world.

The interior and exterior stories complement each other, but they shouldn't be conflated. The scientific version of human creation deeply disturbs some religious people, so they seek ways to reject it and cling to their traditional creation stories. But this is neither good science nor good theology. The scientific version of the cosmic story poses an exciting challenge for theologians and philosophers to rethink our ideas about God and human destiny.[36]

Regardless of their particular faith tradition, says Haught, modern religious communities must not only get their evolutionary science right but embrace its significance or risk becoming irrelevant in an increasingly science-savvy world. They must see (and many already have) that when they cling to literal interpretations of creation myths (which were always meant to be metaphorical) they're being as narrow minded as scientific materialists who cling to the argument that the objective, reductionist version of the world is the only truthful version. The real truth is that the story of our evolving, subjective religious awareness is in consonance with the evolving scientific narrative of the universe.[37]

6

A Deep Dynamic Presence

In the Bhagavad Gita, the Hindu god Krishna and the warrior prince Arjuna talk about ultimate truth and the path to enlightenment. The iconic depiction of this encounter shows Krishna holding the reins of Arjuna's war chariot as they pause between the lines of two vast armies about to clash. Arjuna's princely duty requires him to initiate the battle. But Arjuna has family members and friends on both sides, so he bemoans his fate as the one who must bring terrible harm to so many he loves. Filled with self-doubt, disillusioned to the point of inaction, Arjuna pleads for Krishna to help him make an enlightened, moral decision.

Krishna tells Arjuna that the moral dilemma he sees is an illusion. He must fulfill his sacred duty to God. Seeing the divine nature of all things, beyond the illusions of mortality and materiality, will help him see the correct choice. They discuss the different paths one may take to achieve this spiritual enlightenment, to find the pulse of morality within. But when Arjuna continues to despair, Krishna grants him the power of cosmic vision, allowing him to see the true nature of the universe. Suddenly Arjuna beholds Krishna's ultimate form, the supreme God Vishnu: an infinite and terrifying presence with countless beast and human faces looking in all directions at once; torsos, arms, and legs interconnected yet separate; uniting all the beings and forces of the universe into one supreme god. Arjuna's individual consciousness is immersed into Krishna's timeless, universal consciousness from which all reality is derived. Arjuna briefly attains a state of pure enlightenment that even holy men with lifetimes of meditative practice and Vedic study cannot achieve.

"All material worlds and spiritual worlds flow from my being," Krishna declares. "The other gods that people worship emanate from me. All space and time manifest in me. Behold within me that the coming battle that troubles you so much has already been fought; the dead are on their way to another life, the survivors on their way to eventual death and rebirth."[1]

From this enlightened state Arjuna now understands that the outcome of the battle he must start is preordained, the victors and vanquished already chosen. Humanity's struggles are mere ripples in an infinite cosmic sea. He now grasps that his role in this eternal drama is to become an instrument of Vishnu's divine will. But Arjuna is also a mortal, and mortal minds, particularly those with little meditative training, weren't meant to perceive the true nature of reality. Enlightened yet terrified by this unsettling epiphany, Arjuna begs Krishna to transform himself back into his familiar friend and mentor. Having momentarily perceived ultimate reality, Arjuna knows why he must do his duty and go forth to give battle, but seeing the true nature of reality is also more than he can handle.

"All the planets tremble and so do I," Arjuna gasps. "Please return to your familiar form and…forgive me for not knowing who you really were. Through your gift of universal consciousness, I now understand my duty. But tell me, God of all things, now that I've momentarily experienced the rapture of your divine being, how can I return to that rapturous state? You're so far beyond me, how do I begin to know you?

"Many paths lead to me. You can know me by devoting your life to me, free of all other desires, studying only sacred scripture," Krishna responds. "But this is not your path. You have worldly desires and princely responsibilities. So, through discipline and practice you must learn to see through the illusion of your material self to your true cosmic nature…but you must also do your duty!"[2]

Scholars can't agree on when the Bhagavad Gita first appeared in Hindu scripture. The Kurukshetra War it depicts, an epic battle whose telling resonated through ancient Indian history, occurred about 3000 BCE. But the Gita was written much later, probably around 200 BCE during what some scholars call the Axial Age—the transformative epoch that birthed today's global religions. As with most sacred texts the Gita endures through the ages because it discusses philosophical and spiritual insights that people can readily grasp and be inspired by. Modern scholars and artists have interpreted the Bhagavad Gita—the Song of God—on religious, historical, and metaphysical levels. Most agree that it primarily examines how to find the right path when faced with difficult choices by selflessly fulfilling one's duty to God, expecting no reward other than the sublime satisfaction derived from right work done well. The essence of our being is a soul that lives on after us through cycles of rebirth and death. Evil and suffering enslave us when we allow the selfishness and desire inherent in our transient physical self to overshadow our selfless eternal being. God, as a dimension of ultimate reality, exists in all of us, as Krishna reveals. Connecting with God within you and acting selflessly to embody God's will in the world will help you find the right path.

The moment of Krishna's transformation from Arjuna's friend and mentor into the ineffable, overwhelming vision of "absolute" reality (his *Vishvarupa*), in which all the gods and forces of the cosmos are unified in one supreme deity, embodies metaphysical consilience of monotheism and polytheism, a synthesis of Hindu religious beliefs. Krishna, himself an avatar of supreme lord Vishnu, never commands Arjuna to worship him and him alone. The essence of their dialog is about Arjuna's own enlightenment, how he must seek grace and spiritual meaning from within himself. Krishna, as God's spirit, is within all of us, but how we connect with that spirit is up to us. Unlike the Old Testament Yahweh, Krishna doesn't demand Arjuna reject all other gods. He expects Arjuna to do his duty, but only as a means for Arjuna to find spiritual fulfillment within himself, not as a sacrifice. Morality—how to conduct oneself and know right from wrong—comes from knowing God within oneself; it's not handed down as a set of rules.

Jung as Prophet

Carl Jung said the Bhagavad Gita's depiction of human existence as an inverted tree, with the common roots as our souls extending to the cosmos and the branches forming our individual earthly selves, perfectly describes the juncture of religion and psychology. Religious images and ideas engage the unconscious mind, the inner psyche, he said.[3] People of Eastern religious traditions seem to more intuitively grasp that God speaks to us through the unconscious and is essentially indistinguishable from the unconscious—not the individual unconscious of Sigmund Freud, of repressed childhood and infantile impulses, but what Jung called the "collective unconscious."[4] Jung described this as containing "the whole spiritual heritage of man's evolution, born anew in the brain structure of every individual." To describe the relation of the universal collective unconscious to our individual conscious minds, Jung refers to the mythical image of Adam and Eve. What were their minds like before they ate the forbidden fruit? What were they consciously aware of? What was their relationship with God? The conscious mind of modern humans metaphorically split off from the universal unconscious when God chased Adam and Eve from the Garden. The cares of existence fell upon them; the "minds" they possessed in the Garden were pushed back into unconsciousness, beyond reach of conscious thought. To find existential wholeness in our lives we must make an inner psychic quest to strengthen the bridge to this ancient mind within. Jung said that Christ would never had made the impression he did on his followers if he hadn't expressed something that was alive and at work in their unconscious.[5] Such a statement would certainly offend most Christians, who would likely respond that it was Christ's divine nature, not his ability to make a good impression, that captivated his followers and instilled in them the holy mission of the church. But Jung's statement was much less a religious critique or historical observation than a riddle directed at modern people: The ancients who witnessed Christ were not all that different from us. Therefore, what words would resonate deep within us and inspire us at the most basic level as existentially and spiritually true?

Mainstream psychology marginalized Jung for his freeform blend of science and mysticism and his musings about God and the collective unconscious. But as a prophet and provocateur his insights have stood the test of time. Jung's idea that God is both immanent within us and distant from us[6] seems to resonate with the conclusions of neuroscientists like Fred Previc and Andrew Newberg, who observed that an essential feature of mindfulness and religious meditation is dissolution of the neurologic boundary between immediate self and distant reality. Jung anticipated the spiritual yearning of the Western mind in response to the horrors of WWII and the psychic oppressions of authoritarianism. Particularly in Europe, people were turning away from the religions of their ancestors, observed Jung. The fault wasn't Western religious traditions *per se* but the cultural amnesia that obscured the true source of religious faith, which comes from within ourselves, from the psyche, not as some commodity or item "from the inventory of the outside world."[7] The Eastern mind intuitively knows this, said Jung. The ancestral memory of the Western mind might have understood this at one time, but it's been lost to us. "With us man is incommensurably small and the grace of God is everything; but in the East, man is God and he redeems himself.[8]

In the East, what people call "mind" has largely to do with the undiscovered but vitally expressive unconscious. In the West, "mind" is our immediate thoughts and our awareness of them. The unconscious is largely nonexistent for us, said Jung.[9] In the East God exists as a deep, dynamic presence; in the West we've allowed God to become an abstraction.

God From East and West

The mythologist Joseph Campbell, who devoted his career to studying religious practices, mythology, and symbolism, incorporated Jung's ideas into much of his own writing. Campbell agreed that Eastern religions tend to emphasize directly experiencing or identifying with God while Western Biblical tradition speaks to having a relationship with God.[10] The nuance is subtle but profound, which Campbell highlighted by recounting a meeting with Martin Buber, the Austrian religious and existentialist philosopher.[11] Buber had declared that twentieth century historic and political events had caused God's face to become hidden from modern mankind. We were in "exile" from God, said Buber. Campbell questioned this metaphysical claim by saying that he'd just returned from India, where people seemed to be experiencing God all the time. Buber was affronted that Campbell would deign to compare the Judeo-Christian God with an Eastern conception of God. He simply dismissed as irrelevant Campbell's remark and apparently the deeper implication that the Hindu God and Judeo-Christian God might be the same God; therefore, why should God turn away from one people but not another? People were exiled from God, insisted Buber. How they found their way out of exile was up to them.

A short time after this encounter, Campbell was visited at his home in New York by a Hindu scholar who had immersed himself in the Bible to understand the religious beliefs of his host country. After some polite hesitation, the scholar confessed that he couldn't "find any religion" in the Bible. Campbell explained that in the West, unlike the religious East, reading the somewhat imagined history of the ancient Jewish people is considered a "religious exercise."[12] The lesson from these two encounters with religious scholars, said Campbell, was that what constituted religion for one was no religion at all for the other, largely because of their very different notions of the nature of God. Within the Eastern tradition, God is a divine mystery immanent within each of us, Campbell explained. God isn't somewhere out there in the universe; God is only accessible through inner vision. But no one ever gets "cut off" from God. There's no exile and atonement, no choosing one people over another. Attributing such human traits to the ultimate divine mystery within us would be unthinkable. Western tradition doesn't necessarily demand that we view God as apart from us, but the Bible clearly portrays God as an external presence observing us from above. Moses is never invited to share God's cosmic consciousness as Krishna did with Arjuna. Anthropomorphizing and personalizing God as wholly outside us—imaging God in our own image, said Campbell—diminishes the possibility of experiencing God within one's own being. A God we experience as an immediate, vital presence within us is unlikely to hand down a universal, immutable code of law that must be obeyed for all time.[13]

The metaphysical question of whether humans can have direct inner experience of God has always been a source of conflict in Western religious belief, said Campbell.[14] The discovery that all humans possess a capacity to experience God within themselves, regardless of their individual religious beliefs, could be a unifying force among different religions. But this can't happen if people interpret their sacred texts literally rather than trying to find deeper, allegorical meaning within them.[15] Literal translations tend to have meaning only for a select few; allegorical translations can cross cultural and historic boundaries and have meaning for all people. As an example of early Christian writing that urges practitioners to look beyond immediate and literal understanding of religious practice and seek allegorical meaning Campbell cited the Gnostic gospel of the apostle Thomas, which was much less a narrative of Jesus's life and more a collection of teachings that seem closely associated with Kabbalah, Jewish mystical thought. In a remarkable passage, Jesus tells his followers not to "look to the sky or the sea for the Kingdom of Heaven, because the Kingdom is within you," and "if you know yourselves then you will know you're the sons of the Father and if you don't know yourselves you'll dwell in poverty."[16]

Gnostic Echoes

As a scholar of early Christianity, historian and writer Elaine Pagels participated in translating the gospel of Thomas from its ancient Coptic script, along with many other ancient texts which for centuries had been lumped together as the odd writings of the diverse and somewhat mysterious Christian Gnostic sects that emerged and flourished in the earliest days of the church until they were denounced as heretics and banned by orthodox church authorities in the second century AD. Since earlier generations of scholars had no direct access to the actual texts, they tended to accept the Catholic church's denunciation of Gnosticism as an assortment of eccentric writings outside the mainstream of church doctrine with nothing to offer in terms of serious scholarship or theology. Pagels had also accepted this view until she and her colleagues translated original Gnostic sources themselves. She was surprised, she said, to discover the texts to be rich with meaning and intuitive truth.[17,18] A striking example was Thomas's recounting of Jesus saying that if you bring forth what is within you, what you bring forth will save you, and what you don't bring forth will destroy you.[19] Some Gnostic texts claimed that God bestows a *luminous epinoia* within each human, said Pagels, an ancient Greek term roughly translated as "spiritual intuition." The authors of these texts believed luminous epinoia doesn't necessarily reveal God directly, because God is ultimately incomprehensible to us. Complete identity between God and human is impossible. But by imparting true insight into God's nature, luminous epinoia helps people see the real God behind stories, images, and other things they experience. Pagels explained that disagreement over "spiritual intuition" and whether humans can experience God directly occurred in many early Christian communities, but it was the Gnostics who made the idea of inner knowledge—knowledge not of the intellect but of the heart—the cornerstone of their faith.[20,21] And it was this steadfast vision of God as a divine wisdom within oneself that placed them at odds with the orthodox teachings of

Jews and early Christians who insisted that God was wholly other than humans and forever separate from human nature.[22]

Early church leaders tried to end the dispute by proclaiming that Christians must have faith in the truthfulness of the church's interpretation of the words of the Apostles. The correct path—*the only path*—was to *believe* God existed as a revealed truth, not to *seek* God as a presence within oneself.[23] They banned Thomas's gospel and other Gnostic texts from the church's canon. In doing so, said Pagels, they bolstered church authority, which helped galvanize the fragile and isolated churches throughout the Roman world against the terrifying persecutions they were facing. But they also impoverished them by delegitimizing a path to spiritual insight through which many believers had discovered (and still do) the essence of their faith. For example, many Gnostic-Christian groups had conceived their own versions of *apolutrosis*, a ritual of second baptism that symbolized conjoining with Christ the previously unknown part of one's being discovered through spiritual inquiry.[24] The purpose of apolutrosis was to recognize a person's spiritual growth and rebirth. To Orthodox authorities this practice devalued the common baptism all believers underwent when first joining the church. It also promoted schisms and factionalism as each church created its own version of apolutrosis, they said. But, more concerning, it placed undue emphasis on an individual's spiritual growth at the expense of redemption.[25] Traces of these tensions in the early church still exist in the common set of gospels church authorities chose as the foundation of orthodox belief. Pagels notes, for example, that in one passage of the Gospel of Luke, Jesus tells the Pharisees that "the kingdom of God is within you," (17:20-21 KJV) but elsewhere Jesus implies that the kingdom of God is imminent but separate from the world and people will be harshly judged before entering.[26]

A Distant Mirror

Early church authorities could banish texts and practices that didn't conform to orthodox teachings, but they couldn't banish the spiritual yearning embodied in them. Christian mystics through the ages, such as Teresa of Avila, John of the Cross, and Thomas Merton have pushed the boundaries of "revelation," said Pagels. Yet, unlike the ancient Gnostics, they've stopped short of directly identifying themselves with God,[27] which would put them squarely at odds with fundamental Christian doctrine. Still, the enduring legacy of such mysticism reflects the abiding need of many people within the Christian community (and within the Jewish and Islamic communities as well) to seek God on their own, not necessarily outside the boundaries of acceptable doctrines of faith perhaps, but in ways that are validated by their own life experience.[28] The fact that some people feel they must pursue this spiritual growth on their own as seekers, while others prefer to participate as believers in more traditional forms of worship and practice, only speaks to the wealth and diversity of our religious traditions, said Pagels.

After reading her brilliant essays on early Christianity, I would add that any claim that either the "seeker" or "believer" approach is exclusively correct denies the reality of actual church history. As Pagels points out, most denominations today, as always, abound with competing views and singular claims about who best understands Jesus's teachings.

Pagels uses her remarkable talent as a writer to energize distant historic events and bring an engaging immediacy and urgency to esoteric theological questions. Her narratives about early Christianity—*The Gnostic Gospels, Beyond Belief,* and *Revelations: Visions, Prophecy, and Politics in the Book of Revelations*—are marvels of historic scholarship on their own. But, to borrow historian Barbara Tuchman's phrase, they're also distant mirrors of our own times, as we come to see that in many ways the philosophical clashes of early Christianity, inextricably bound to the political and social turmoil of the late Roman Empire, reflect the religious and philosophical tumult of our own age. In both eras we see people divided on the nature of God and whether God is accessible through orthodox practice or individual experience. A recent Pew study showed that while 80 percent of Americans say they believe in God, only 56 percent say they believe in God as depicted in the Bible, which the study interpreted to mean a God who is directly active in human affairs.[29] The remainder conceive God to be a spiritual presence who may or may not directly engage with humans or influence human events. Another Pew survey showed that about 75 percent of Americans believe they talk to God,[30] which means a large percentage of people who don't believe in the Biblical God still believe in a God accessible through their thoughts and prayers.

Church authorities in the fourth century managed to finally ban "unorthodox" gospels and religious literature related to Christian practice, and temporarily calm the currents of dissent. But as history plainly shows, the stream of new understandings of old ideas, theological disputes, and spiritual restlessness never stopped flowing. Those who believe today's widespread questioning of orthodox faith and decline of organized religion signal an end to religion are looking at their own history through a clouded lens. The value of Pagels' scholarship is in how it reveals the ongoing tension between "seeker" and "believer" to be a powerful and mostly positive source of creative energy and change within the Christian tradition.

Altruism Transformed

Many of us might identify with the spiritual-seeking independence of the ancient Gnostics. But if we seek a sense of the divine that resonates with our own life experiences, what experiences are we talking about? The First Noble Truth of Buddhism is the existence of suffering, not just our own suffering but the suffering that permeates the world. You don't need to practice Buddhism to grasp that this seems fundamentally correct. Humanity's universal experience of suffering is woven into the fabric of religious belief. Suffering is an obvious fact of existence, if not within ourselves, surely as a primary experience of others. Christianity and Judaism may not consider the existence of suffering to be a doctrinal truth, but responding to the challenge posed by human suffering is an essential part of both religions.

As Pagels explained in *Beyond Belief*, the altruism and charity of early Christians to ease the suffering of others helped transform them from a persecuted minority to a respected and vital social movement. As a Jew preaching to other Jews, Jesus often invoked God's command to love mankind, comfort the sick, feed the hungry. As early Christianity spread through the Roman world, transforming from a rebellious faction to a universal religion, this message of altruism and charity, clearly and unarguably from Jesus's mouth, became a fundamental precept of Christian faith. When plague swept through the Roman world in the second century, killing between a third to half its population from Asia Minor to Gaul, the persecuted and reviled Christians stayed in the cities, caring for the sick and burying the dead, while their pagan neighbors fled for their lives. In the aftermath, Galen, the Greek-Roman philosopher and physician to the imperial family, gave the Christians grudging praise for their contempt of death and their stoic self-discipline and sense of justice.[31] As many writers have observed, despite the faults of the Christian church then and now, the early Christian call to altruism, charity, and personal sacrifice was a defining feature of the new civilization that emerged from the declining Roman world, even if practitioners didn't always live up to their professed values.

It wasn't that Roman paganism was bereft of morality. But Christian faith commanded compassion and empathy for *all* people, not just fellow Christians—a universal humanism unheard of in the ancient world, crossing all lines of ethnicity, social caste, and wealth.[32] Some writers have attributed this solely to the Christians' certainty of life after death and an everlasting spiritual existence in heaven. This claim not only overestimates the psychological potency of delayed gratification and reward but turns a blind eye to the fact that morality and codes of conduct are primary features of all religions. In the Bhagavad Gita, morality flows as a duty from one's sense of being with God. As Neuroscientists like Andrew Newberg and Fred Previc have shown, deep religious experience is accompanied by feelings of altruism and love for others. As van Huyssteen explains, religions are organized systems of beliefs, symbols, and practices that don't so much rely on a supernatural component as belief in a "super-empirical"[33] order that guides human life. As we know in modern times, it's entirely possible for a successful society to operate on a secular moral code, just as long as most people agree on a conceptualized (super-empirical) sense of right and wrong and how things should be. (Although some religious writers might insist that these intuitive secular codes of conduct in secular societies are just reverberations of longstanding Christian traditions.)

Suffering as an Existential Truth

Theologians have written volumes about why Judeo-Christian morality rose to prominence in Western civilization. So, from an abundance of respect for this scholarly tradition I'll refrain from adding my negligible insights about it and consider the broader question of the synchronicity of morality and awareness of suffering that runs through all religions and why some argue that it demonstrates why science can never fully explain religion.

Circling back to the passages from the Bhagavad Gita we see the ego at the center of the consciousness field, as Jung might put it, troubled because it's intelligent enough to anticipate the consequences of choices it feels compelled to make and morally attuned to the suffering it might cause. Arjuna has a warrior's courage and no concern for his own life. But the idea of inflicting suffering on others deeply troubles him. It's for this reason that Krishna makes him see that war and death are inevitable. His sensitivity to suffering isn't wrong, but the only way to truly deal with suffering is to pursue the divine path through duty to God. The point of his psychic journey wasn't simply to see God or achieve a state of diminished ego selflessness; it was to help him find the right course of action in the mortal world. As Trappist Monk Thomas Keating said, the spiritual life recognizes that the human appetites that lead to suffering are an illusion; we can detach ourselves from them, but we shouldn't expect them or the suffering they cause to go away. We don't know where the world is headed, but we must take responsibility for it with no expectation that we'll evolve out of suffering, said Keating. What we hope for is to develop our capacity to help the world cope with suffering.[34]

Neuroimaging can document how a devoted practitioner achieves a selfless state of mind to experience only the conscious flow of existence. But what neuroimaging can't show or explain is how achieving this heightened state also heightens the moral senses, which it invariably does. One can't practice mindfulness if one isn't aware of human suffering and social injustice, wrote Vietnamese monk and Buddhist scholar Thich Nhat Hanh in *Living Buddha, Living Christ*. Proper mindfulness imparts understanding and compassion.[35] Awareness of suffering and awareness of one's own implication in suffering as a human being is the thread that runs through all religious belief, said Thich. Jesus and Buddha both grasped that suffering is pervasive.[36] Offering a way out was an essential theme of their teachings. From the outside it might seem wonderful to be a monk or nun and learn to look deeply within yourself, said Thich. But the purpose of the meditation or prayerful contemplation, in part, is to be able to peer deeply into the nature of suffering. A contemplative life doesn't mean abandoning the work that needs to be done in the world.[37]

You don't need to practice a religion or believe in Jesus or Buddha to be touched by Thich Nhat Hanh's words. Most of us are naturally moved by stories of compassion and sacrifice. But why? Why do we "naturally" feel this way? And, more important, why are so many of us inclined to *act* to relieve the suffering of others? This is a big deal for the evolutionary psychology of religion because people jeopardizing their own safety (i.e. their reproductive success) to help others—plague victims in ancient Rome or coronavirus victims in 2020 New York City—doesn't make biological sense. Throughout history, many altruistic people have claimed to be driven by their religious beliefs. But evolutionary psychology requires answers grounded in science. So, in purely biological, non-religious terms, what's going on?

The Biology of Altruism

Altruism and sacrifice are defining features of social animals. Darwin couldn't explain why some animal species existed as social groups because social living requires varying amounts of sacrifice—suppressing one's own reproductive success for the benefit of the group.[38] This was especially true for "eusocial" insect colonies Darwin observed in which some members seemed genetically predetermined to sacrifice all of their own reproductive capacity to help ensure the reproductive success of others. Individual group members suppressing their own reproductive needs for the group didn't fit with evolutionary theory. If one's genes are the ultimate determinants of one's behavior (whether insect, bird, or human), and the very essence of natural selection is always directed towards preserving and passing along one's genome, how would a gene that codes for a behavioral trait that suppresses or interferes in some way with one's own reproduction be preserved and passed along through multiple generations to become widely distributed through members of a species?

Evolutionary psychologists, social scientists, and sociobiologists theorize that social animals from ants to humans carry suites of genes that promote altruistic behaviors. Competition between individuals in the group is balanced by an ingrained need to cooperate and even sacrifice for the overall good. But how would such an anti-Darwinian urge gain a foothold in the genome of a species and become widespread? A parent might sacrifice its life for an offspring, or siblings might sacrifice themselves for one another because, from a strictly genetic point of view, their genomes are closely related enough to make it worth the sacrifice. One genome is lost but two or more very similar genomes are preserved. The math behind the genetics makes sense. But the math falls apart when we consider altruism spread across an entire population. By what biological reasoning can we explain one genome being lost to preserve the unrelated genomes of distant cousins and relatives? If modern religious altruism has biological roots, then the hard science must support the social theory.

Religion as Kin Selection

A theory called inclusive fitness and kin selection that emerged in the 1960s said that the math can work when the sum total of the benefits to the reproductive fitness of the entire group outweighs the cost to the reproductive fitness of those making the sacrifice. An individual is more likely to make sacrifices for close kin than distant kin, but in any group there are enough kin related to enough group members making the sacrifice to make the theory work. The math was complicated, and it involved a bit of wishful thinking, but from studies of ants and other insect populations there was enough evidence to persuade biologist E. O. Wilson to include kin selection in his groundbreaking book *Sociobiology: The New Synthesis*, published in 1975, which served as a founding text for the exciting new scientific subspecialty of sociobiology, which studies the underlying biological determinants of social behavior.

As Wilson himself recounts, he found the idea of inclusive fitness "enchanting," but was troubled by the lack of clear empirical evidence supporting it.[39] Many of his sociobiologist colleagues weren't as circumspect so, for the next three decades, the theory of inclusive fitness witnessed its own evolution from intriguing idea to scientific dogma. Academic careers were built on inclusive fitness, said Wilson. International prizes awarded. Science writer Richard Dawkins eagerly incorporated the idea into his globally famous book *The Selfish Gene*. Although the evidence was shaky and largely hypothetical, there was absolutely no doubt in the minds of many theorists that altruistic religious behavior could be explained by kin selection and inclusive fitness algorithms. For example, a paper published in 2014 in the journal *Animal*

Behavior[40] theorized that belief in God is conceptually synonymous with kinship. It speculates there must have been nine phenotypes of behaviors, such as empathic connections, theory of mind, and social learning, that were already present in human populations before distinctly religious behaviors appeared and took hold. Practicing religion (serving God) helps overcome the bio-social roadblock of what to do when one's group gets so large that it's impossible to identify all of one's kin. Because everyone in the group worships the same God, then serving God becomes a surrogate for serving one's kin. Perhaps more important, although one's kin may not always be monitoring one's behavior, an all-knowing, all-seeing deity doesn't miss a thing. Genetic kinship is gradually replaced by psychological kinship as group inclusion relies more upon shared religious concepts than kinship. The rise of monotheism in the West represents the growing predominance of psychological kinship over genealogical kinship, the study concluded. Universal religions offer inclusive fitness benefits to larger, more diverse groups of people. Thus, the vast complexity of global religious belief can ultimately be traced back to the prime genetic drivers of kin selection and inclusive fitness.

This paper was eloquent and brilliantly reasoned. But it rested on suppositional sand, as did many similar studies, because in 2010 Wilson and a team of mathematicians and theoretical biologists at Harvard showed that the underlying genetic-algorithmic logic of inclusive fitness and kin selection doesn't work.[41] Virtually all of the animal social phenomena inclusive fitness claims to explain can also be explained more accurately and simply by traditional genetic inheritance models. A major flaw with the mathematical modeling of inclusive fitness is that it can tempt scientists to see cause-effect relationships between genetic events where they don't actually exist.

When Wilson and his team published their findings debunking inclusive fitness in The Proceedings of the National Academy of Sciences, one of the America's most prestigious scientific journals, they sought to puncture the protective academic bubble that had grown around the subject. For decades, sociobiologists working in the field had found virtually no evidence of inclusive fitness actually occurring in animal populations. Throughout the early 2000s many of these scientists tried to publish their observations, only to have them critically marginalized or rejected by the scientific peer review establishment that controlled the publishing process and who had become enraptured by the inclusive fitness "dogma," said Wilson.[42]

But, as the 2014 paper I described demonstrates, this severe theoretical blow didn't make inclusive fitness go away. The belief that human altruism and religion can ultimately be explained in genetic-biological terms has attained ideological status among many in the scientific community, despite its mathematical debunking. While sparse, there's enough random evidence of inclusive fitness working in the animal world to make it plausible for humans, they argue. The fact that the math of its underlying genetic logic is highly questionable, at best, doesn't seem to matter.

And so…if inclusive fitness is bad biology, can sociobiology—or any biology—fully explain human altruism?

Morality is Biologically Unique

As primatologists like Jane Goodall saw with modern chimps, members of pre-human social groups continuously balanced their own needs versus the needs of the group. The group offered stability and protection, but for young, healthy members in their reproductive years this meant giving up some of their food and resources, including labor and risk-taking, to remain accepted members of the group. Relationships were tense and shifting, always balancing competition with cooperation. Nepotism—favoring one's kin over others—occurred within the overall framework of internal competition, but it wasn't the only factor. If internal competition between group members grew too intense, the whole group suffered and risked perishing. Individuals with the right mix of altruistic versus competitive behavior tended to have more progeny and thereby pass on their behavioral traits. Individual reproductive survival was thereby determined by both individual-level selective competition within the group and group-level selection as groups of pre-humans competed with other groups for the same resources and environmental space. Increased competitive behavior helped *individuals* survive; increased altruistic behavior helped *groups* survive.[43]

In Wilson's words, for individuals within the group, surviving and thriving demanded a good memory and good predictive abilities to assess the intentions of other group members and to inwardly rehearse various competitive scenarios that might happen.[44] In simplest terms, we became the social animals we are because of the adaptive advantages of possessing a complex social intelligence. It allowed us to communicate, compete, cooperate, recognize, and evaluate amongst ourselves in ways that made us the first globally dominant species, said Wilson. There's no doubt that the rudiments of our social-behavioral traits, including religious behavior, evolved from our pre-human ancestors. But even with sophisticated technologies it's nearly impossible to create an algorithmic grid that irrefutably shows how a selected trait evolved over time. The decline and fall of inclusive fitness muddles the cognitive science/evolutionary psychology version of how human beings became religious beings, which has caused many behaviorists and cognitive theorists to denounce Wilson's claims (although Wilson himself is an agnostic) rather than question their own presumptions. Wilson agrees that humans seem to be instinctively religious—that our brains seem "made" for religion—but adheres mostly to the evolutionary psychology view that this probably has more to do with group behavior and tribalism than innate spirituality which, in Wilson's mind, makes religion more troublesome than beneficial. Still, he concludes, there's more to religion than just its biological roots.[45]

For scientific atheists, the problem with *not* being able to explain religion in terms of inclusive fitness or some other genetic model is that it leaves open the possibility that there's something intangible and unanalyzable about religious behavior. It gives breathing room to theological explanations, as I described in Chapter three.

Even within a strictly biological framework, we can say that our biologically unprecedented level of self-awareness combined with our biologically unprecedented cognitive fluidity means that we *experience* the world in biologically unprecedented ways. And it is from this biologically unprecedented experience of the world that our morality, spirituality, and religious awareness arise. People might perform acts of charity because they believe a deity is watching, but they also might perform them out of an enlightened sense of being in the world—something that science can't possibly account for. Therefore, trying to find biological or sociobiological precedents with which to explain our biologically unprecedented moral awareness will never succeed. As van Huyssteen observed, no scientific explanation can fully account for the moral and religious dimensions of our existence.[46] Our morality is a distinctly human, biologically unique feature of human consciousness. This doesn't mean we're free of other biological influences, but our actions simply can't be explained entirely within the context of those influences. We possess an epiphenomenal awareness. Because of the unique way we experience the world we're compelled to judge our own actions by standards beyond ourselves.[47]

Referring again to the words of Thich Nhat Hanh, when we focus only on the rituals, symbols, and outer forms of religious practice, we stop receiving and embodying the spirit of the tradition within that religion.[48] This goes for religious practitioners of all faiths, but I would add that it also applies to scientists seeking to explain religious behavior in biopsychological terms by focusing only on behaviors, rituals, myths, and altruistic cost-benefit tradeoffs. The internal rationality of religious behavior, to borrow van Huyssteen's term, must be experienced directly to be explained.[49]

Recalling van Huyssteen's description of the theology of the great Jewish scholar Abraham Heschel, we shouldn't be overly concerned with humanity's biological origins. The driving question before us isn't how we're similar to animals, but how we're different.[50] We need to be focusing on our humanity, not our animality. What is it that's "human" about a human being? In this sense, said van Huyssteen, the search for human origins will never be complete without the search for human destiny.

7

Vocatus atque non vocatus...

A few months after my son Gregory died, I began to feel a desperate need to be with other bereaved parents. My wife and I couldn't decide if we were now ghosts in the land of the living or awakened beings in a world of sleepwalkers. Either way—my sense of detachment from others, even close friends, who had not experienced the loss of a child compelled me to seek out those who had. I was lonely for others of my kind.

I began attending local chapter meetings of Compassionate Friends, a national volunteer network established to help bereaved parents cope with their grief. During those tearful meetings I heard others talk about their bewilderment and even frustration at how to respond to the well-meaning but misplaced wishes of family and friends who wanted them to find peace or heal or come to terms with their loss.

How, we wondered, do bereaved parents explain that we're no longer the people we once were? Perhaps to family and friends we seemed distracted or diminished. Or perhaps, as we believed, we had gained a painful but liberating new awareness that made us seem distracted or diminished. Either way, despite what those close to us desired, we couldn't come back from where our grief had taken us. We couldn't unlearn our new understanding of the world. Coping with our loss meant learning to live a new life in an estranged and alien world.

As I began to outline this book, I realized our conversations at Compassionate Friends revealed how much our culture denies the reality of death. Over and again I listened to parents recount needing to hide their grief to protect the feelings of those who'd never experienced catastrophic loss. Like it or not the illusions that come from living within a materialist culture were shattered for us. We understood, for example, when a mom who'd lost her twenty-year-old daughter rolled her eyes in frustration as she recounted the shock her friends and family expressed when she announced she probably wouldn't continue the chemotherapy treatments she'd started before her daughter died. The mom didn't want to die. She had much to live for, she assured us. But the physical and emotional hassles of chemotherapy might distract her from more important things. Her family members were appalled at this socially unacceptable nonchalance. What could be more important than fighting cancer and living as long as you possibly can? But we bereaved parents totally got what she was saying. It's not about being depressed or psychologically dissociated from life. We all valued our own lives and hoped to stick around to be with our loved ones. But death was no longer the unmentionable, terrifying opposite of life. We'd learn to live with death. We had no choice. Death was the faces of our beloved children, and so we learned to accept it and open ourselves to a very different version of reality.

Cynics often denounce religion as crutch for those who can't face death. What's implied in their words is that religious believers lack the courage to face non-existence or that they're too gullible or naïve to see the fallacy in ancient fairytales about invisible souls living beyond the loss of the physical body.

They're missing a crucial point. Yes, perhaps we just cease to exist when we die. Or, maybe there's an afterlife. As a person trained in science and as a person of faith, I have no problem living with both ideas in my head, and I'm quite certain I'm not alone.

But I also believe most people practice religion because it opens a dimension of sanctity and meaning in *this* life. What happens in the next life—if anything happens at all—isn't the point. For bereaved parents religion heightens the awareness that your encounter with your child was a sacred encounter, a beautifully resonant and meaningful encounter. Religion reminds you that we walk in mystery throughout our lives and there's nothing mundane or ordinary about any of it. For many bereaved parents, life becomes overwhelmingly spiritual, and fear of death becomes the furthest thing from their minds. Because I was raised a Catholic, I found the familiar ritual of Catholic mass helped me transcend the mournful present. Prayers and words resonated more deeply. The turmoil in my heart gave way to feelings of deep gratitude for having walked with my son in this life, talked with him, loved him. The joy he gave me would briefly come back to me and ease the pain of losing him. In those moments I also sensed some important truth, felt but not verbally explainable, hovering just beyond my conscious grasp.

Vocatus atque non vocatus, Deus aderit read the inscription on Jung's doorway. "Summoned or not, God is here." Jung most certainly would have clarified this: Whether you believe in God or not, God is within you even if you've buried your awareness of God beneath a mountain of rationalist denial and logic. The spiritual world is the real world; the day-to-day world is the illusion.

I don't wish to suggest some morbid connection between death and religious awareness. On the contrary. What I realized after listening to the heartfelt words of other bereaved parents was that our spiritual lives express the degree to which we have come to understand that the felt experience of God is primary to everything else, and that in an illusory universe—the realm of fluctuating phenomenon, as Francisca Cho describes it—in which change and dissolution are inevitable, the only enduring reality is awareness of God's existence and that we are, somehow, embodiments of that existence. True, our felt awareness of God's existence can't make pain and suffering go away, but it helps us endure them. When Gregory played a thundering Rachmaninoff concerto, God experienced the joy. When I found Gregory's lifeless body on that terrible winter morning, God shared my devastation. I believe we all have an inner awareness of God's presence to varying degrees, but our awareness tends to become clouded and cluttered with the practical demands of our lives, our reasoned beliefs, our emotional turmoil. Prayer, meditation, religious ritual, cosmic contemplation—these things can help us move the clutter aside. Sometimes life events cut through the clutter whether we're ready or not. For many of us, perhaps most of us, the clouds never entirely get out of the way (to paraphrase Joni Mitchell's dreamy song lyric). Immersing oneself in an entirely rationalistic worldview—an understandable tendency for people in science and technology—can cause you to believe you must suppress this urge for inner awareness. Explain it away. The clouds become the only thing you allow yourself to see.

All grieving parents must come to terms with the realization that things aren't going to work out as they once thought. Life isn't going to go according to plan. They must find a new kind of faith; a faith that embraces grief as well as joy, chaos as well as hope; a faith that's immediate and accepting. Ask a parent who has lost a child if, given the choice, they would do it again. Would they have the child, raise the child, love the child knowing they were going to suffer all the pain and devastation of losing the child? All the grieving parents I've asked, without hesitation answered yes. I can only explain their response like this: The love far outweighs the grief. Bringing that love into the world, experiencing it, even if it's only for a short time, overshadows the grief and regret. What every grieving parent understands in their own way is that life is sacred. Their eyes are opened to a new understanding that human life is miraculous, incomprehensible.

When I could open my own eyes again, I wondered, as a writer, how I might describe my altered sense of reality. It was the same world I'd lived in, but it was a transformed world. God was no longer comfortably distant, out there in the universe, guarding its secrets, balancing the moral scorecard, soothing the anxieties of those who prayed. God was immediate, immanent, familiar yet existentially different, a deeply mysterious and loving presence.

How do I explain this? From a psychological perspective it's quite normal for grieving parents to undergo religious experiences as a result of dealing with grief, trauma, and dissociation from reality. This is a charming and perfectly reasonable clinical observation that explains away religious belief by framing it as an extreme emotional response. In time, hopefully, the parent's "normal" connection to reality returns. But I was a quietly religious person before I became a grieving parent, and I understood where my grief had taken me. What I experienced was something I couldn't adequately explain until I read the insights of theologian Paul Tillich.

Paul Tillich and a God Outside of Time

Tillich said we must all find the courage to accept life without being "conquered" by life—neither giving in to the fascination of life nor the anxiety of death. Find the courage, in other words, to fully embrace the reality that life is both creative and destructive; freedom is tempered by destiny, chance with necessity, responsibility with tragedy. It may sound trite, but Tillich was saying that you must learn to ride the metaphysical wave.[1]

Karen Armstrong and others who write about modern religious belief speak of a "God-shaped hole" in the hearts and minds of Western people which causes us to feel alienated from ourselves and morally detached from the world.[2] It's not that we've all stopped believing in God (although many have), but that for many people the place God once occupied in our hearts and minds is now empty. We might argue how this happened—rationalism, the rise of science, the horrific events of the twentieth century— but there's little disagreement that it *has* happened. God stopped being a felt presence and became a distant and explainable object, a hypothesis one can choose to accept or reject. Armstrong said Tillich was one of the great modern theologians to first bear witness to this estrangement.[3]

As a young army chaplain in the trenches of World War I, Tillich witnessed the carnage and suffering that inspired his revelation that secular humanism and Europe's rationalist enlightenment were deeply flawed. The God who'd lived within this narrow philosophical framework—the detached, objectified God he'd prayed to as a boy and studied as a university student—was dead. This was the same God we create to meet our moral expectations and soothe our existential fears, the kind of agent-God imagined by cognitive theorists. The real God, the God who shows up when the imagined God withers away, is the source of all being, said Tillich. Within us and without us, grounded in our deepest sense of existence, in every aspect of joy, sorrow, suffering, and despair that defines each of us as human. To find this God we must lose our illusions of God and have the courage to follow our religious awareness where it takes us.[4]

I think Tillich's ideas hint at how a scientific worldview might be infused with meaning. For example, there's a scientific argument that time doesn't exist—or, at least, it doesn't exist as we experience it. Time is a dimension as physically real as space. But because we can't move around in time like we can in space—back and forth, up and down—we experience it in one direction. Once something has happened it recedes into the past and ceases to exist. In fact, nothing ceases to exist, it just exists at another point in time which we can't get to.

Tillich said our inability to see time for what it really is causes us to believe that time will inevitably stop for us; everything we are and everything we've done will dissolve into nothingness. So, he asked, how do we find meaning in life when we believe that whatever meaning we've found is destined to slip away? Meaning comes to us when we realize we exist within God's awareness, said Tillich.[5] God exists throughout time and is aware of each moment of our lives and, therefore, each moment is affirmed in eternity. God enters our human time and elevates it to eternal time. This sounds remarkably similar to Alfred North Whitehead's idea that the continuous transformation of conscious experience in the world becomes woven into God's substance. Tillich and Whitehead were contemporaries (Whitehead was older), but I've found no evidence that they directly influenced each other. I suspect the similarity of their ideas about the nature of God reflects the first tremors of the science-inspired disruption of the West's long-held perception of the universe as a predictable clockwork with a distant, invisible God at the helm.

Can Scientific and Religious Communities Work Together?

Many scientists say human existence has no purpose or meaning in the grand scheme of things. The only meaning life can have is what we attach to it, and we must recognize that any meaning our imagination conjures dies with us. There's no "ultimate" meaning. But here's where theology can rescue science: why is "the grand scheme of things" somehow more significant than our own brief existence? If we intuitively suspect that there is something special about our existence, that our self-awareness with its three billion years of phylogenic history is telling us something, then why are we so quick to discount it in favor of newly acquired information derived from a relatively new mode of thinking that has no use for concepts like "meaning" and "purpose"? We don't need to embrace creation myths and magical thinking, but why not put more faith in intuitive wisdom informed by, not based on, scientific insight?

The bare-bones scientific story of human existence says we're the pumped-up descendants of a line of intelligent, self-aware apes who for a very brief moment in our short and pointless existence have figured out how to observe enough about the universe to grasp that it's got nothing to do with us. Hardly an inspiring story.

I love astronomer Neil deGrasse Tyson's documentaries about planets, galaxies, and the cosmos. His warm personality and easy-going brilliance pull you in and keep you glued to the screen. But I always find myself wondering why, like other "public" astronomers, he always finds it necessary to diminish our planet, our solar system—our significance—to leverage the majesty of astronomical space. Public scientists in other fields tend to do the same thing, as if diminishing us and marginalizing our importance somehow makes the subject at hand more appealing. Why not pull us into the story by reminding us that all of nature, including us, is amazing and mysterious—not just the subject at hand—and perhaps mention how wonderful it is that we exist to be able to perceive and appreciate it all? From a theological perspective, the idea that there's nothing special about human existence is easily on par with any of the naïve creation myths that scientists like to make fun of. Scientists, particularly biologists, climatologists, and environmental scientists understand that humans urgently need to grasp the gravity of climate change and take more responsibility for the planet. But why? If scientists are also saying that life is meaningless, how can they expect to succeed? Why should we take them seriously?

Rather than diminishing us or scolding us or scaring us, what scientists most urgently need to do is *connect* us. Show us how deeply connected we are to nature, whether it's tadpoles in a pond or galaxies hundreds of light years away. This is what biologist Ursula Goodenough brilliantly did with *The Sacred Depths of Nature*, her book about the deep interconnectedness of all life, from the molecular to the ecological levels. Each chapter describes essential concepts of evolution, with an emphasis on vertebrate and ultimately human evolution, and ends with a poem or prayer imbedded in a spiritual reflection. Goodenough, a "religious naturalist," says she finds no need to resolve within herself the contradictions or "immiscibilities" between different versions—religious, scientific—of how we see nature and our role in it.[6]

The Battle Ahead

I was horrified when, in 2017, President Trump casually brushed aside the bootless protests of the global scientific community and pulled America out of the Paris Climate Agreement, declaring it a "bad deal."[7] The shock wasn't that a science-denying, anti-intellectual politician would do such a thing. The shock was how easily the dedication, hope, and exhaustive work of thousands of scientists could be dismissed in the name of greed and short-sighted self-interest. I thought of French philosopher Simon

Weil's brilliant insight: "Imaginary evil is romantic and varied; real evil is gloomy, monotonous, barren, boring."[8]

A recent Pew Research Center study showed that self-identified practitioners of most religious faiths, which probably included many in Trump's political base, overwhelmingly favor stronger environmental regulations.[9] But why isn't this attitude reflected in our national politics? Is it because the scientific worldview lacks a human-centric meaning compatible with religious belief? Wouldn't it be amazing, in response to the unfolding global environmental catastrophe, if the two establishments saw each other as allies rather than rivals? How might that happen?

At the very least we need more writers and generous public intellectuals like Ursula Goodenough and Joan Roughgarden who have illustrated with their thoughtful prose that our deepest religious beliefs are wonderfully compatible with the scientific truth of evolution.

In *The Sacred Depths of Nature*, Goodenough proposes a planetary ethic, informed by evolutionary science yet respectful of individual traditions, that provides a shared spiritual orientation for facing global threats such as climate change, nuclear war, genocide, and pandemic disease.[10] Among the many excellent points she raises is that describing the underlying biology of the world shouldn't diminish our enthrallment and sense of magic and wonder from our experience of the world. Although she never entirely strays from her scientist's perspective, her words show how this point of view needn't demean or refute a religious perspective.

In *Evolution and Christian Faith*, Joan Roughgarden says that with climate change and environmental chaos, Christians now face the defining moral issue of caring for God's creation.[11] God is an experience, says Roughgarden, not an idea.[12] Evolution may have a direction and be guided by God, but those are theological and religious questions, not scientific ones. The secular study and teaching of evolution should never involve looking for evidence to prove or refute God's existence.

I agree with her that Intelligent Design and Creationism advocates seem biologically naïve when they base their proof on gaps in the evolutionary record or the emergence of some seemingly inexplicable appendage or behavior. All it means is that the tedious work of filling in the gap or explaining the appendage hasn't been done.[13] I've had only a brief encounter with comparative evolutionary studies, but I totally get what she's saying. Pointing out the gaps is easy; filling in the gaps takes lots of training and hard work. Although she declines to discuss her personal views on the nature of God, I think she touches upon an elegant way of explaining God's hand in nature when she describes the ideas of Catholic theologians who propose that nature is a conduit between the human mind and God's mind, and that studying nature helps us know God.[14] The science informs our theological view of evolution, but the science view isn't designed to reveal God's presence.

Like Goodenough, she sees no personal conflict between religious belief and a firm, traditional science version of evolution. She says the Bible supports the idea that Christians have a moral responsibility to care for the planet. If Christians believe God intended the earth to be as it is, for the diversity and abundance of species to be as they are, then how do we respond to the massive ecological destruction we've caused? You can't read Genesis without concluding that a despoiled polluted Earth was not God's plan.[15]

Evolution as Dark Ideology

Lastly, I strongly agree with Roughgarden that scientists must do a better job convincing the lay public that evolution isn't about "survival of the fittest,"[16] which in fact describes neither the actual evolutionary process nor innate human nature. The truth is that all species, all living things, are expressions of the interconnected, ever-changing phenomenon of life. Evolution describes the complex network of biophysical dynamics beneath this miraculous phenomenon. The fact that a few isolated species stick around a little longer than others (a.k.a. survival of the fittest) doesn't remotely describe what's actually going on. Yet, this hyper-simplistic interpretation of Darwin's theory has been grossly misapplied to the human condition to justify oppression, social violence, and genocide ever since it was conceived in the late nineteenth century.

In Darwin's time there was little understanding of the genetics of speciation and population biology, no knowledge of cell biology, and no knowledge of molecular biology. His observations about the apparent competitiveness within and between species in nature were generally correct, but he lacked any understanding of the underlying biological processes. "Survival of the fittest" is a childishly simplistic vessel to contain all we now know about evolution. In terms of defining human behavior, yes, humans compete with each other; but we also deeply depend on each other for survival and absolutely require each other for our own intellectual development and emotional health. The unvarnished anthropological truth is that humans are intensely social animals who never would have made it out of the Neolithic era without our genetically programmed urge for altruism.

Evolutionary psychology tells us that the human story is much more about cooperation than competition. It also tells us that altruism is one of the biological roots of religious belief and behavior. But to recall the words of van Huyssteen and Rabbi Abraham Heschel from chapter six, biology alone cannot explain the human dimension of religious altruism. As neuroscientist Fred Previc noted when he observed the neurological correlates of religious belief, people experiencing religious feelings associated them with a sense of openness to the world and oneness with others. This observation has been echoed in many neuroscience and cognitive science studies. Respect for human dignity, one of the foundations of monotheism, rests upon empathy—the deeply human capacity to feel "one" with others. Empathy and a sense of oneness could serve as an emotional boundary marker, a reality check for people of faith, to let them know when their religious belief has devolved into ideological bias, which inevitably divides humanity into "us" and "other."

The Power of Fear

We'll need a lot more altruism and empathy in this new century. In his excellent historic essay "Black Earth: The Holocaust as History and Warning," Yale historian Timothy Snyder warns that twenty-first century people have gravely misunderstood the events that took place in Germany in the 1930s.[17] Faced with the perceived environmental threats of economic collapse and loss of food and other resources, an educated society very much like ours embraced a ruthless tyrant's claims that an innocent ethnic "other" in their midst was plotting to undermine their world: Germans must awaken to the existential fact that life is nothing but a never-ending racial struggle, said Hitler…survival of the fittest. And they must do whatever is necessary to win.

Today we all understand that the Nazis' "survival of fittest" philosophy was nothing more than racist political dogma masquerading as scientific theory. But it's also a horrifying cautionary tale of cynical political authorities appropriating scientific theory to justify their actions. It's perilous to ignore what science is telling us but it's equally perilous to misinterpret what we're being told.

Snyder's research revealed how educated and seemingly enlightened people can gradually descend into moral chaos when they feel threatened by "others." Don't think it can't happen again, warns Snyder. Don't think it can't happen here. Don't think we're morally superior to the Europeans who succumbed to madness.[18]

What I found particularly chilling was Snyder's observation that American cinematic and popular culture is rife with dark visions of a violent, post-catastrophic world. This pessimistic subliminal projection isn't a healthy sign, he said, nor is our growing tolerance for genocide and mass displacement in the developing world and the reemergence of right-wing racism and hate speech in the West.[19]

Echoes of Snyder's warning reverberated in our response to the 9/11 terrorist attacks. Our shock and altered sense of reality from the magnitude of the destruction led to a period of graceful mourning with victims' families. Unfortunately, our grace gave way to national paranoia and blind vengeance. We declared a "war on terror" which still defines much of our foreign policy and domestic politics two decades later. We talked ourselves into believing that our enemy wasn't just a fanatical, politicized fringe but an entire religious multitude with whom we'd shared the planet for over a thousand years, yet of whom we knew very little. We were entirely correct to have pursued the perpetrators and done everything necessary to protect the country from a recurrence. But in the heat of the moment we allowed cynical policy makers to exaggerate the danger we were facing for their own purposes and, worse, marginalize the diversity and humanity of the global Islamic community. We became morally detached spectators as our government officially committed torture, kidnapping, and false imprisonment, culminating in the national shame of Abu Ghraib. Our dollars funded a conflict that destabilized the Middle East and directly or indirectly caused the deaths of hundreds of thousands of innocent Muslims and thousands of our own soldiers.

It took years for our culture to recover from the blow to our national pride and to reinfuse our foreign policy with morality and respect for human dignity. The lesson wasn't that America is an immoral country. We're a very decent and moral country. The lesson was how easily our inherent morality was subverted when our sense of stability was threatened and our self-image was challenged.

Journalist Dexter Filkins brought a worldly perspective to our loss of self-image with his description of the World Trade Center ruins, still smoldering as darkness came over the city.[20] Conditioned by years of reporting from the Middle East, his first thought was how familiar it seemed. If he let his mind drift he could almost imagine being back in Afghanistan or India or

Turkey, where mass death from bombings, earthquakes, and famines happened all the time. People in those countries lived with this kind of trauma; for us it seemed like the end of civilization, he said. Recalling my own memories of that day, I'd say Filkins was spot on. It wasn't just the loss of life that induced our national trauma; it was the shattering of our worldview that bad things aren't supposed to happen to good countries. He was also correct that horrifying tragedies like this happened all the time in the developing world, where most people live with a visceral familiarity with death and terror. This is the violence and despair that drives refugees to the southern borders of America and Europe. In the coming decades these are the people who will suffer first and most from the effects of climate change, as a recent Papal encyclical, *Laudato Si*, warned. And as Timothy Snyder asks: Will we see them as "other"?

Refugees aren't a recent phenomenon. In the 1940s and '50s Paul Tillich observed the world's refugees who'd been displaced by war and persecution. We could learn much from them, he said, because they're more in touch with life and death. Death has grasped the reins of their lives. They wander the world seeking sanctuary but often die when artificial walls stop their wandering, he said.[21] Life seldom works out for them; it doesn't go according to plan. Many are deeply religious, not because they're poor and uneducated but because they see the world as it is. They are the generation of the "end," said Tillich, the death camp survivors and displaced immigrants, and we deceive ourselves if we think we're different and can't ultimately share their fate. We deceive ourselves if we believe these people only need help and refuge. What they and we need most is love, said Tillich.[22]

Belief in God doesn't stop bad things from happening. It won't stop climate change from happening. It didn't stop the holocaust from happening. It can't shield us from murderous, emotionally unbalanced fanatics, whether they're Islamist killers or right wing hatemongers. But how we assimilate our faith into our worldview makes all the difference in how we respond when bad things blow our illusions away.

Dig the Well Before You're Thirsty

About a year after Greg's death the worst of all possible coincidences occurred. A friend I'd known since college, who had provided great comfort in my loss, called to say that he'd now joined me in the world of the forever bereaved. His son Josh had been killed when he was thrown from his truck on the way to work. He hadn't been wearing a seat belt. He'd probably been startled by a deer darting from the woods to cross the road.

When I visited Mark on his farm in Virginia shortly after, we passed several nights in deep conversation about our wonderful boys, religion, the recklessness of young men, and the expectation that perhaps we'd someday be with our sons again. We talked of cosmology and the spiritual meaning of evolution. Vodka made the conversation flow. Mark and I had met in a vertebrate anatomy and evolution class at Boston University taught by Dr. Richard Estes, a famous paleontologist and gifted educator. Through the years, through jobs, marriages, and children, Mark and I had kept up the conversations we'd started as students over coffee or beers after hours of lab work examining dinosaur skulls and dissecting sharks and salamanders.

On my second night in Virginia, as he was showing me the ornamental pear trees Josh had planted along the driveway leading into the farm, Mark confessed that through years of study, work, and family he'd never abandoned his religious beliefs or his faith in God's existence. The pain of Josh's death was almost unendurable, but his faith had anchored him against the storm. He wondered how someone without faith could endure a child's death. I said I didn't know; I'd come close, but I was grateful that I'd never completely abandoned my Catholic roots. What Mark said next was profound. He wasn't sure if it was an ancient Buddhist or Chinese proverb, but it was this: dig the well before you're thirsty.

"True," I agreed, and thought, *Amen, Brother. Absolutely right!* Don't deny your spirituality. Don't reason away your faith, because sooner or later you'll discover that life isn't reasonable. The world isn't rational. Sooner or later you'll need a well of strength to drink from, and you won't get it from a scientific theory or something you read on Wikipedia.

But how do you create a well of spiritual strength when the best scientific evidence tells us there's no invisible God out there running the universe and enforcing cosmic laws, no afterlife, no transcendence, no reality other than physical reality, no meaning other than what we make up to distract ourselves from non-existence? How is it still possible to have faith?

I hope some of the ideas I've outlined in this book show that faith in God and trust in scientific evidence are not only compatible but can complement each other in ways that enrich one's life experience. What science tells us about the world is correct, but only within the framework of what can be perceived

185

through a scientific lens. Science can't explain human consciousness and, therefore, how we perceive and believe in God. Science can describe how evolution transformed stardust and water into self-aware beings, but it lacks all resources to explain what this miraculous event means. Science is just a way of seeing the world; faith is a way of knowing the world.

I've approached this project as a journalist reporting on the clash of ideas among scientists who study the psychological phenomenon of religious belief. I've included the thoughts of non-scientist scholars and writers whose work, to me, brought crucial context and insight to the scientific debate. None of these ideas are my own. I'm humbled by their brilliance and deeply grateful for the generosity of spirit that moved writers such as Joan Roughgarden, Elaine Pagels, Andrew Newberg, and Wentzel van Huyssteen to open their hearts and minds to all of us. Academic scholars owe their allegiance to academia; scientists owe their allegiance to scientific integrity; journalists owe their allegiance to telling a good story. I hope this has been a good story.

Symbiosis or Extinction

Another writer I briefly mentioned was Dr. Lynn Margulis, a professor of evolutionary biology my friend Mark and I had known at college. She was, hands down, one of the most important biologists of our time. Because of her gender she never got the recognition she deserved. It was Margulis who discovered that mitochondria, the "energy factories" of eukaryotic cells (the kind of cells in our bodies) had first evolved as separate, bacteria-like prokaryotic organisms. At some point they symbiotically fused themselves into the progenitors of eukaryotic cells. Had this not occurred, evolution would have taken a dramatically different course. The scientific establishment laughed when she announced her theory until molecular biological studies showed she was correct. She fought and usually won many similar battles in her career, earning a reputation as a brilliant but fearsome intellect. I remember her students adored her.

One of the many books she'd written before she died in 2011 was *Symbiotic Planet*, in which she described Gaia theory, which roughly says that the web of biophysical interactions among all living things, from soil bacteria to blue whales, comprises a self-regulating, global physiological system. Gaia adjusts ocean temperatures and atmospheric oxygen and carbon dioxide. Astronomers can predict fluctuations in atmospheric and temperature conditions on other planets in our solar system based solely on physical factors—gravity, rotation, energy from the sun, chemical elements in the atmosphere and on the surface—mainly because those planets are biologically inert. Dead. Not so with Earth. The complex interplay of living systems and ecosystems creates a self-adjusting, geophysiological system. We're unpredictable because we're alive. Gaia has a kind of consciousness—not the human kind, but a dynamic responsive-awareness emergent from the interconnected activities of all the organisms on the planet.[23] Margulis hated that people might infer New Age mystical ideas from Gaia theory or make some connection to the ancient cultural notion of Mother Earth. Gaia is strictly science, she insisted, and very complicated science. If you don't want to learn about the chemical interplay of soils, algae, bacteria, plants, animals, atmospheric gases, and population dynamics then don't bother with Gaia. You need the details to see the big picture.

What struck me about Margulis's description of Gaia was her frustration that the global scientific community had little use for Gaia theory. Exploring it fully to appreciate how it really works and what it might tell us will require specialists in biology, chemistry, geology and other fields to overcome academic apartheid and understand each other's science, and that just wasn't happening, she said. Specialists don't want to stray from their fields.[24]

I couldn't avoid the irony in her complaint. Margulis often railed against religion. Unfortunately, like most scientists, the religion she railed against was one-dimensional and unsophisticated, full of myths and superstitions, a straw dog set up to be knocked down by a scientific worldview.[25] It's unfortunate she never wanted to stray from her field...

She ended *Symbiotic Planet* with cynical reassurance: Gaia is infinitely stronger than us. Nothing we can do—nuclear war, climate change or other environmental catastrophes—will ultimately destroy Gaia. She's a tough bitch, said Margulis. Life on Earth doesn't depend on us. We can destroy ourselves by disrupting Gaia with our waste, but the planetary web of bacteria, plants, and other organisms will gradually restore her balance once we're gone.

This is old news, but it had special poignancy coming from such a brilliant scientist. Yes, I thought, we'd all be gone...*but so would all our scientific knowledge.* And it will have been the practical and technological applications of that knowledge that did us in—not our religious beliefs, but scientific knowledge scrubbed and sterilized of all meaning and morality.

Seeking a Metanarrative

The last writer I'll mention is Pope Benedict XVI, the "intellectual" pope who led the Holy See in the years between Pope John Paul and Pope Francis. Benedict observed that modern people want to lay down the burden of faith yet remain within the "fabric of faith." The burden they want to lay down, he said, is the emotional and intellectual conflict that comes from trying to reconcile traditional religious beliefs passed to us from ancient times with contemporary cultural and scientific worldviews. The important question, said Benedict, isn't how we resolve the disconnect between ancient and modern, but to ask why people simply don't put down the burden and turn their backs on faith altogether. The answer, he explained, is that all people need meaning in their lives, and not just factual or "objective" meaning. They want to believe in a meaning that "knows and loves me."[26]

Benedict was speaking to the global Catholic community, but his insights were relevant to the entire Western monotheistic tradition: Catholics, Jews, Protestants, and all the sects and denominations within them. The meaning contained within the ancient wisdom of our deepest religious beliefs has withstood the test of time. This is the meaning Benedict was referring to. This is the meaning that's being lost, one that faithfully accepts and embraces our intuitive awareness of a reality beyond physical reality.

The power of these insights hits home when we consider the astonishing diversity and breadth of books, blogs, journals, and websites created by people who, one way or another, want to reconcile science and religion. In our postmodern bewilderment, where truth is relative and reason is no longer absolute, many people no longer accept the disconnected narratives of traditional philosophy, religion, or science.[27] We're all seeking our own meta-narrative that can provide coherence and keep us within the fabric of faith.

What would such a story of faith tell us? Perhaps it should be written as a poem and not a scientific theory or religious belief. I feel deeply blessed to have had the opportunity to study science and to walk in the woods and swim in the ocean and see the amazing biodiversity around me through a scientist's eyes. But I have no illusions that a scientific grand narrative can become a metanarrative of science and faith. Science endlessly fractures the world into shimmering wonders and processes within processes. We need a story that tells us how it all blends together into a transcendent unity, otherwise we'll become like Poe's dreamer within a dream, stranded on the beach, with all our scientific knowledge slipping through our fingers like grains of sand, drawn out to the infinite sea.

Acknowledgments

My intent for this book was to immerse the reader in the clash of ideas among scientists and scholars of religion about the nature of religious belief in light of new revelations from evolutionary psychology and cognitive science. The spectrum of information relating to this debate is populated mostly with books and other works created by and for specialists. My vision was to make this fascinating topic available to a wider audience. In that regard, J. Wentzel Van Huyssteen's *Alone in the World? Human Uniqueness in Science and Theology* provided the philosophical grounding from which to cast a broad net in these turbulent waters to catch the shimmering questions at the heart of the debate. No matter how firmly you hold your beliefs about God and science in human religious experience, Dr. Van Huyssteen will broaden your horizons. I join with many others in thanking him for transcribing his Gifford Lectures, delivered at the University of Edinburgh in 2004 to fulfill the endowment's intent to explore new concepts in natural theology, into a book that will serve as a cornerstone of the subject for years to come.

I send my deep gratitude to Heather Shaw for her incisive and insightful editing and for being a superb audience of one. Sincere thanks to Emily Hitchcock at Boyle & Dalton for supporting this experiment in metaphysical journalism. And to my loved ones near and distant who, as always, endured my emotional absence and moodiness, thank you for my freedom and for your graceful presence in this world.

Endnotes

PROLOGUE

1. Klass, D. *The Spiritual Lives of Bereaved Parents*. 1st ed., Routledge, 1999, p. 50.

CHAPTER ONE

1. Andrews, P. W., and J. Anderson Thomson Jr. "Depression's Evolutionary Roots." *Scientific American*, 2010. https://www.scientificamerican.com/article/depressions-evolutionary-roots/.

   Eagles, J.M. "Seasonal Affective Disorder: A Vestigial Evolutionary Advantage." *Medical Hypotheses*, vol. 63, no. 5, 2004, pp. 767-772. https://www.sciencedirect.com/science/article/abs/pii/S0306987704004013.

2. Margulis, L. *Symbiotic Planet*. Basic Books, 1998, Nook ed., p. 104.

3. Bae, B., et al. "Genetic Changes Shaping the Human Brain." *National Center for Biotechnology Information,* 2015, pp. 423-434. https://www.ncbi.nlm.nih.gov/pmc/articles/ PMC4429600/; https://www.ncbi.nlm.nih.gov/books/ NBK234146/.

4. Zaidel, D. W., et al. "An Evolutionary Approach to Art and Aesthetic Experience." *Psychology of Aesthetics Creativity and the Arts*, vol. 7, no. 1, 2013, pp. 100-109.

5. Beattie, T. *The New Atheists*. Orbis Books, 2008, pp. 150-154.

6. Ibid. p. 150.

7. Gould, S. J. *Rock of Ages: Science and Religion in the Fullness of Life*. The Random House Publishing Group, 1999, Nook ed., p. 27.

8. Ibid. p. 22.

9. Novak, D. "Germans Against Hitler: The Witness of the White Rose." *First Things,* 1990. https://www.firstthings. com/article/1990/04/germans-against-hitler-the-witness-of-the-white-rose.

10. Armstrong, K. *The Case for God*. Alfred A. Knopf, 2009, Nook ed., p. 159.

11. Woit, P. "Hawking Gives Up." *Not Even Wrong*, 2010. https://www.math.columbia.edu/~woit/ wordpress/?p=3141, and, Muehlhauser, L, Stephen Hawking—The Grand Design (Review), 2010, http:// commonsenseatheism.com/?p=12325.

CHAPTER TWO

1. "Larycia Hawkins." *Wikipedia.* https:// en.wikipedia.org/w/index.php?title=Larycia_ Hawkins&oldid=720567464.

2. Lind, D. "Donald Trump's Proposed 'Muslim registry,' Explained." *Vox*, 2016.

3. Graham, R. "The Professor Suspended for Saying Muslims and Christians Worship One God." *The Atlantic*, 2015. https://www.theatlantic.com/ politics/archive/2015/12/christian-college-suspend-professor/421029/.

4. An, K. "Professor 'Flabbergasted' Over Wheaton's Plans to Fire Her Over Worship Comments." *The Washington Post*, 2016.

   An, K. "Do Muslims and Christians Worship the Same God? College Suspends Professor Who Said Yes." *The Washington Post*, 2015.

   Felton, R. "Chicago Christian College Suspends Professor After Headscarf Comment." *The Guardian*, 2015.

   Parshman, M. B. "Wheaton College Seeks to Fire Christian Professor Over View of Islam." *Chicago Tribune*, 2016.

5. Schmid, A.P. Phd. "Radicalisation, De-Radicalisation, Counter-Radicalisation: A Conceptual Discussion and Literature Review." *International Centre for Counter-Terrorism - The Hague*, 2013.

"Cultural Theory after 9/11: Terror, Religion, Media; Substance." *The Johns Hopkins University Press*, vol. 37, no. 1, 2008. https://www.jstor.org/stable/

CHAPTER THREE

1. Goodall, J. *Reason for Hope.* Warner Books, 1999, pp. 73-76.
2. Ibid. p. 76.
3. Ibid. p. 160.
4. Ibid. pp. 180-181.
5. Wong, K. "Tiny Genetic Differences Between Humans and Other Primates Pervade the Genome." *Scientific American*, 2014. https://www.scientificamerican.com/article/tiny-genetic-differences-between-humans-and-other-primates-pervade-the-genome/.
6. Wade, N. *Before the Dawn: Recovering the Lost History of Our Ancestors.* Penguin, 2007, pp. 74-78.
7. Caron, F., et al. "The Reality of Neanderthal Symbolic Behavior at the Grotte du Renne, Arcy-sur-Cure, France." *Plos One*, 2011. https://doi.org/10.1371/journal.pone.0021545.
8. Mithen, S. *The Prehistory of the Mind.* Thames & Hudson, 1999, Nook ed., pp. 155-160.
9. Sankararaman, S., et al. "The Date of Interbreeding between Neandertals and Modern Humans." *Plos Genetics,* 2012. https://doi.org/10.1371/journal.pgen.1002947.

10. van Huyssteen, J. W. *Alone in the World: Human Uniqueness in Science and Technology.* Wm. B. Eerdmans Publishing Co., 2006. p. 139.

11. Beattie, Op. Cit. p. 150.

12. van Huyssteen, Op. Cit. pp. 247-251.

13. Ibid. pp. 176-193.

14. Armstrong, K. *A History of God.* Ballantine Books, 1993, Nook ed., p. 24.

15. Campbell, J. *The Mythic Image.* MJF Books, 1974, pp. 6-8.

16. Armstrong, Op. Cit. p. 22.

17. Ibid. p. 29.

18. Ibid. p. 28.

19. Boyer, Op. Cit. p. 38.

20. Dawkins, R. *The God Delusion.* Houghton Mifflin, 2008, Nook ed., p. 19.

21. Dennet, D. C. *Breaking the Spell.* Penguin, 2006, Nook ed., p. 24.

22. Rupke, J. "Religious Agency, Identity, and Communication: Reflections on History and Theory of Religion." *Taylor & Francis Online*, vol. 45, no. 3, 2015.

23. Thompson, B. N. "Theory of Mind: Understanding Others in a Social World." *Psychology Today,* 2017. https://www.psychologytoday.com/us/blog/socioemotional-success/201707/theory-mind-understanding-others-in-social-world.

24. Bednarik, R. G. "An Aetiology of Hominin Behaviour." *HOMO—Journal of Comparative Human Biology*, 2012, pp. 319-335.

25. Boyer, Op. Cit. pp. 32, 64.

26. Ibid. p. 194.

27. Ibid. p. 16.

28. Ibid. p. 23.

29. Botero, C. A., et al. "The Ecology of Religious Beliefs." *PNAS*, 2014.

30. Whitehouse, H., et al. "Complex Societies Precede Moralizing Gods Throughout World History." *National Center for Biotechnology Information,* 2019, pp. 226-229.

31. Ge, E., et al. "Large-Scale Cooperation Driven by Reputation, Not Fear of Divine Punishment." *The Royal Society Publishing,* 2019. http://doi.org/10.1098/rsos.190991.

    Yali, D., et al. "The Competitive Advantage of Institutional Reward." *The Royal Society Publishing,* 2019. http://doi.org/10.1098/rspb.2019.0001.

    De Cruz, H., and J. De Smedt. "Supernatural Punishment: What Traits are Being Selected." *Taylor & Francis Online,* 2011, pp. 75-77.

32. Boyer, Op. Cit. p. 253.

33. Tillich, P. "Art and Ultimate Reality." *The Museum of Modern Art,* Lecture, 1959, p. 5. https://assets.moma.org/momaorg/shared/pdfs/docs/press_archives/2449/releases/MOMA_1959_0015.pdf.

34. Hanh, T. N. *Living Buddha, Living Christ.* The Berkley Publishing Group, 1995, Nook ed., p. 33.

35. Armstrong, Op. Cit. pp. 334-336.

36. Bargh, J. A., and E. Morsella. "The Unconscious Mind." *National Center for Biotechnology Information*, vol. 3, no. 1, 2008, pp. 73-79. https://www.ncbi.nlm.nih.gov/pmc/articles/PMC2440575/.

37. Jones, J. W. *Can Science Explain Religion.* Oxford University Press, 2016, p. 113.

38. Newberg, A., et al. *Why God Won't Go Away.* Ballantine Books, 2001, Nook ed., p. 102.

39. Jones, Op. Cit. p. 112.

40. Ibid. p. 113.

41. Ibid. p. 123.

42. Ibid. p. 125.

43. van Huyssteen, Op. Cit. p. 275.

44. Ibid. p. 263.

45. van Huyssteen, J.W. "What Does it Mean to Be Human." *Smithsonian Museum of Natural History*, 2020. http://humanorigins.si.edu/about/broader-social-impacts-committee/members-member-resources/wentzel-van-huyssteen-emeritus.

46. van Huyssteen, J. W. *Alone in the World: Human Uniqueness in Science and Technology.* Wm. B. Eerdmans Publishing Co., 2006, p. 260.

47. Ibid. p. 192.

48. Ibid. pp. 265-266.

49. Ibid. p. 249.

50. Ibid. pp. 196-197.

51. Ibid. pp. 102, 265, 275.

52. Merali, Z. "Did a Hyper-Black Hole Spawn the Universe." *Nature,* 2013. https://www.nature.

com/news/did-a-hyper-black-hole-spawn-the-
universe-1.13743.

53. Fingelkurts, A., and A. Fingelkurts. "Is Our Brain
Hardwired to Produce God or is Our Brain Hardwired
to Perceive God? A Systematic Review on the Role of the
Brain in Mediating Religious Experience." *ResearchGate*,
vol. 10, no. 4, 2009, pp. 293-326.

54. van Huyssteen, Op. Cit. p. 312.

55. Roughgarden, Op. Cit. pp. 30, 31, 89.

56. Heschel, A. J. *God in Search of Man*. Farrar, Straus and
Giroux, 1955, p. 279.

57. van Huyssteen, Op. Cit. p. 297.

58. van Huyssteen, Op. Cit. p. 8.

CHAPTER FOUR

1. Previc, F. H. "The Role of Extrapersonal Brain Systems
in Religious Activity." *National Center for Biotechnology
Information*, 2006, p. 513.

2. Parker, A. *In The Blink of An Eye: How Vision Sparked the
Big Bang of Evolution*. Basic Books, 2003.

3. Feinberg, T., and J. Mallatt. "The Evolutionary and
Genetic Origins of Consciousness in the Cambrian
Period over 500 Million Years Ago." *Frontiers in
Psychology*, vol. 4, 2013, pp.1-27.

4. Ibid.

5. Mashour, G. A., and M. T. Alkire. "Evolution of
Consciousness: Phylogeny, Ontogeny, and Emergence
from General Anesthesia." *PNAS*, vol. 110, 2013.

6. Ibid.

7. Ibid.

8. Ibid.

9. Herculano-Houzel, S. "The Remarkable, Yet Not Extraordinary, Human Brain as a Scaled-Up Primate Brain and its Associated Cost." *PNAS*, vol. 109, 2012.

10. Kurzweil, Ray. "Get Ready for Hybrid Thinking." *Youtube,* uploaded by TED, 2014. https://www.youtube.com/watch?v=PVXQUItNEDQ.

11. Kurzweil, R. *The Singularity is Near.* Penguin, 2005, Nook ed., p.27.

12. Ibid. pp. 29-48.

13. Herbert, F. *Dune.* The Berkley Publishing Group, 1965, Nook ed., pp. 20-21.

14. McCaslin, T., et al. "Transmitting Fibers in the Brain: Total Length and Distribution of Lengths." *AI Impacts.* https://aiimpacts.org/transmitting-fibers-in-the-brain-total-length-and-distribution-of-lengths/#easy-footnote-1-1118.

15. Purves, D., et al., editors. *Neuroscience.* 2nd ed., Sunderland, 2001, ch. 6. https://www.ncbi.nlm.nih.gov/books/NBK10799/.

16. Linden, D. J. "The Singularity is Far: A Neuroscientist's View." *Kurzweil,* 2011. https://www.kurzweilai.net/the-singularity-is-far-a-neuroscientists-view.

17. van Huyssteen, Op. Cit. p. 111.

18. Roughgarden, Op. Cit. p. 65.

19. van Huyssteen, Op. Cit. p. 147.

20. Ibid. p. 140.

21. Ibid. p. 133.

CHAPTER FIVE

1. Harris, Sam, host. "Conscious: A Conversation with Annaka Harris." *Making Sense,* episode 159, 2019. https://samharris.org/podcasts/159-conscious/.
2. Nagel, T. *What is it Like to Be a Bat.* Reclam Phillip Jun., 2016.
3. Harris, A. "Consciousness Isn't Self-Centered." *Nautilus,* 2020. http://nautil.us/issue/82/panpsychism/consciousness-isnt-self_centered.
4. Desmet, R. "Alfred North Whitehead." *Stanford Encyclopedia of Philosophy,* 2018. https://plato.stanford.edu/entries/whitehead/.
5. Freestone, J. M. "How Princeton Neuroscientist Michael Graziano uncovers the Magic of the Human Consciousness." *Prospect,* 2020. https://www.prospectmagazine.co.uk/philosophy/michael-graziano-attention-schema-magic-human-consciousness-rethinking-interview.
6. *Accelerating Research on Consciousness.* Templeton World Charity Foundation. https://www.templetonworldcharity.org/our-priorities/accelerating-research-consciousness.
7. Hameroff, S., and R. Penrose. "Consciousness in the Universe: A Review of the 'Orch Or' Theory." *Physics of Life Reviews,* vol. 11, no. 1, 2014, pp. 39-79.
8. Ibid.
9. Jedlicka, P. "Revisiting the Quantum Brain Hypothesis: Toward Quantum (Neuro)biology." *Frontiers in Molecular Neuroscience*, vol. 10, art. 366, 2017, pp. 1-8.

10. Meijer, D. K. F., and S. Raggett. "Quantum Physics in Consciousness Studies." *Quantum Mind.* http://quantum-mind.co.uk/quantum-physics-in-consciousness-studies-book/.

11. Meijer, D. K. F., and H. J. H. Geesnik. "Consciousness in the Universe is a Scale Invariant and Implies and Event Horizon of the Human Brain." *Neuroquantology,* vol. 15, no. 3, 2017, pp. 41-79.

12. Dor-Ziderman, Y., et al. "Mindfulness-Induced Selflessness: A MEG Neurophenomenological Study." *Frontiers in Human Neuroscience,* 2013, vol. 7, art. 582, pp. 1-17.

13. Previc, Op. Cit.

14. Viegas, J. "Comparison of Primate Brains Reveals Why Humans Are Unique." *Seeker,* 2017. https://www.seeker.com/health/mind/comparison-of-primate-brains-reveals-why-humans-are-unique.

15. Previc, Op. Cit.

16. Ibid.

17. Ibid.

18. Newberg, Op. Cit. p. 12.

19. Ibid. pp. 11-14.

20. Ibid. pp. 7-12.

21. Ibid. pp. 100-103.

22. Ibid. p. 102.

23. Ibid. pp. 100-103.

24. Newberg, A., and M.R. Waldman. *How God Changes Your Brain.* Ballantine Books, 2009, Nook ed., p.10.

25. Newberg, Op. Cit., *Why God Won't Go Away.* pp. 34-35.

26. Newberg, A., and M. R. Waldman. *How Enlightenment Changes Your Brain.* Penguin, 2016, Nook ed., pp. 20-21.
27. Newberg, Op. Cit., *Why God Won't Go Away.* pp. 108-117.
28. Fingelkurts, Op. Cit.
29. Ibid.
30. Ibid.
31. Ibid.
32. Haught, J. F. *The New Cosmic Story.* Yale University Press, 2017, Nook ed., p. 23.
33. Ibid. pp. 16-25.
34. Ibid. p. 181.
35. Ibid. pp. 23-24.
36. Haught, J. F. *Science and Faith.* Paulist Press, 2012, Nook ed., p. 9.
37. Haught, Op. Cit., *The New Cosmic Story.* pp. 24-29.

CHAPTER SIX

1. Prabhavanada, S., and C. Isherwood. *Srimad Bhagavad Gita: The Song of God.* Ditzion Press, 2013. https://www.bhagavad-gita.org/.
2. Ibid.
3. Jung, C. J. *The Portable Jung.* edited by Joseph Campbell, translated by R. C. F. Hull, Penguin, 1971, pp. 642-643.
4. Ibid. pp. 45, 647, 648.
5. Ibid. p. 615.
6. Ibid. p. 648.

7. Ibid. p. 466.
8. Ibid. p. 486.
9. Ibid. p. 491.
10. Campbell, J. *Myths to Live By.* The Joseph Campbell Foundation, Stillpoint Digital Press, 1972, Nook ed., p. 103.
11. Ibid. pp. 98-99.
12. Ibid.
13. Ibid. pp. 96-100.
14. Ibid. p. 103.
15. Ibid. p. 255.
16. Campbell, Op. Cit., *The Mythic Image.* p. 62.
17. Pagels, E. *Why Religion.* Harper Collins, 2018, Nook ed., p. 168.
18. Pagels, E. *Beyond Belief.* Random House, 2003, p. 32.
19. Ibid. p. 32.
20. Ibid. pp. 75, 164-167, 177.
21. Pagels, Op. Cit., *Why Religion.* p. 168.
22. Pagels, E. *The Gnostic Gospels.* Random House, 1979, Nook ed., p.17.
23. Pagels, Op. Cit., *Beyond Belief.* pp. 29, 129.
24. Ibid. pp. 136, 139.
25. Ibid. p. 141.
26. Ibid. p. 51.
27. Ibid. p. 75.
28. Ibid. pp. 75, 183.
29. "When Americans Say They Believe in God, What Do They Mean." *Pew Research Center*, 2018. https://www.pewforum.org/2018/04/25/when-americans-say-they-believe-in-god-what-do-they-mean/.

30. Ibid.
31. Pagels, Op. Cit. pp. 8, 9.
32. Holland, T. *Dominion*. Basic Books, 2019, Nook ed., pp. 24-25.
33. van Huyssteen, Op. Cit. p. 291.
34. Keating, T. *Reflections on the Unknowable*. Lantern Books, 2014, pp. 11-12.
35. Hanh, Op. Cit. pp. 28, 60.
36. Ibid. p. 42.
37. Ibid. pp. 42, 104.
38. Nowak, M. A., et al. "The Evolution of Eusociality" *National Center for Biotechnology Information*, 2010.
39. Wilson, E. *The Meaning of Human Existence*. Liveright Publishing, 2014, Nook ed., p. 43.
40. Crespi, B., and K. Summers. "Inclusive Fitness Theory for the Evolution of Religion." *Animal Behavior*, vol. 92, 2014, pp. 313-323.
41. Nowak, Op. Cit.
42. Wilson, Op. Cit., *The Meaning of Human Existence*. p. 43.
43. Ibid. p. 21.
44. Ibid. p. 14.
45. Ibid. pp. 94, 95, 96.
46. van Huyssteen, Op. Cit. pp. 275, 288-291.
47. Ibid. p. 291.
48. Hanh, Op. Cit. p. 106.
49. van Huyssteen, Op. Cit. p. 269.
50. Ibid. p. 297.

CHAPTER SEVEN

1. Tillich, P. *The New Being.* Hayaton, 2014, Nook ed., pp. 44-46.
2. Armstrong, Op. Cit., *A History of God.* pp. 18-19.
3. Ibid. p. 423.
4. Tillich, Op. Cit., *The New Being.* pp. 41-42. Henderson, C. P. *God and Science: The Death and Rebirth of Theism.* Ch. 6, J. Knox Press, 1986. http://www.godweb.org/Tillich.htm.
5. Tillich, Op. Cit. p. 123.
6. Goodenough, U. *The Scared Depths of Nature.* Oxford University Press, 1998, Nook ed., pp. 14, 65, 184-185.
7. Duke, R. "Leaving the Paris Agreement is a Bad Deal for the United States." *Foreign Policy,* 2019. https://foreignpolicy.com/2019/05/19/leaving-the-paris-agreement-is-a-bad-deal-for-the-united-states/.
8. Weil, S. *La Pesanteur et La Grace.* Philaubooks, 2018, Nook ed., p. 59.
9. "Views About Environmental Reguation." *Pew Research Center*, 2014. https://www.pewforum.org/religious-landscape-study/views-about-environmental-regulation/.
10. Goodenough, Op. Cit. pp. 184-188.
11. Roughgarden, Op. Cit. pp. 97.
12. Ibid. p. 11.
13. Ibid. pp. 63-64.
14. Ibid. pp. 44-45.
15. Ibid. pp. 95-96.
16. Ibid. p. 89.

17. Snyder, Op. Cit. pp. 12-14.

18. Ibid. p. 315.

19. Ibid. pp. 321-340.

20. Filkins, D. *The Forever War.* Vintage Books, 2008, p. 44.

21. Tillich, Op. Cit. p. 126.

22. Ibid. p. 128.

23. Margulis, Op. Cit. pp. 106-109.

24. Ibid. pp. 108-109.

25. Ibid. pp. 8-9.

26. Ratzinger, J. *Introduction to Christianity.* translated by J. R. Foster, Ignatius Press, 2004, p. 80.

27. Vanhoozer, Op. Cit. pp. 26-33.

About the Author

George Tyler is a science and health writer and former medical researcher who lives in Essex Junction, Vermont. He holds degrees in biology, biochemistry, and journalism and has won awards for editorial and news writing from the Vermont Press Association.